A Pioneering
PLANTSMAN

Arthur K Bulley
(1861–1942)

A Pioneering PLANTSMAN

A K BULLEY AND THE GREAT PLANT HUNTERS

BRENDA McLEAN

The Royal Botanic Gardens,
Kew
The Royal Botanic Garden,
Edinburgh

London: *The* Stationery Office

© Brenda McLean 1997

Applications for reproduction should be made in writing to
The Stationery Office Limited, St Crispins, Duke Street, Norwich NR3 1PD.

ISBN 0 11 250018 8
Cataloguing in Publication Data
A CIP catalogue record for this book is available from the British Library.

Brenda McLean has asserted her right under the Copyright, Designs and Patents Act 1988 to
be identified as the author of this Work.

Edited, designed and produced by The Stationery Office
Designer: Richard Jones

Published by The Stationery Office and available from:

The Publications Centre
(mail, telephone and fax orders only)
PO Box 276, London SW8 5DT
General enquiries 0171 873 0011
Telephone orders 0171 873 9090
Fax orders 0171 873 8200

The Stationery Office Bookshops
49 High Holborn, London WC1V 6HB
(counter service and fax orders only)
Fax 0171 831 1326
68-69 Bull Street, Birmingham B4 6AD
0121 236 9696 Fax 0121 236 9699
33 Wine Street, Bristol BS1 2BQ
0117 9264306 Fax 0117 9294515
9-21 Princess Street, Manchester M60 8AS
0161 834 7201 Fax 0161 833 0634
16 Arthur Street, Belfast BT1 4GD
01232 238451 Fax 01232 235401
The Stationery Office Oriel Bookshop
The Friary, Cardiff CF1 4AA
01222 395548 Fax 01222 384347
71 Lothian Road, Edinburgh EH3 9AZ
(counter service only)

Customers in Scotland may
mail, telephone or fax their orders to:
Scottish Publication Sales
South Gyle Crescent, Edinburgh EH12 9EB
0131 479 3141 Fax 0131 479 3142

Accredited Agents
(see Yellow Pages)

and through good booksellers

DEDICATED TO LOIS BULLEY

WHO GAVE HER FATHER'S GARDENS

TO THE UNIVERSITY OF LIVERPOOL

AND FOR THE ENJOYMENT OF THE PUBLIC

THE GREAT PLANT COLLECTORS

Already published in this series:
'Chinese' Wilson: a life of Ernest H Wilson 1876–1930
by Roy W Briggs

The Great Plant Collectors series is a joint venture between the Royal Botanic Gardens, Kew, the Royal Botanic Garden, Edinburgh and *The* Stationery Office.

Contents

List of Plates

List of Maps and Diagrams

∽ Preface ∽

'A plant-hunter! What is that?'
'We have heard of fox-hunters, of deer-hunters, of bear
and buffalo-hunters ... of a plant-hunter never.'
'No, my boy reader — my plant-hunter — to his labours the whole civilised
world is indebted — yourself among the rest ... They have not only imparted
to us a knowledge of the world's vegetation, but have brought its rarest
forms before our very eyes.' (MAYNE REID, 1858)[1]

This was the introduction to a Victorian boys' adventure story. It was written at a time of intrepid explorations in far-flung places, expansion of the Empire, and triumphant returns with many trophies, including plants. Sir Joseph Hooker had collected wondrous rhododendrons in the Himalayas ... new and rare species never seen before in Britain.

This was the age into which Arthur Kilpin Bulley was born. Few people have heard of him, but early this century his patronage of plant hunters was crucial when there was no government money available. He was an ardent amateur gardener, fascinated by alpine plants, excited by new introductions and keen to add to the wealth of plants in our gardens. Moreover, he had the necessary knowledge, competitive urge, drive and enterprise; he was a colourful character, a cotton broker in the great commercial port of Liverpool. As an enthusiastic socialist, Bulley once confided, 'I have made more money than the heart of man can desire, and I want to do something with it.'[2]

Bulley paid professional plant hunters to collect in remote mountain areas of western China and the Himalayas, Tibet and Burma ... in promising places not yet harvested. It was Bulley's fortune and foresight which sent out the then unknown George Forrest to collect in the mountains of Yunnan. He launched Frank Kingdon Ward on his plant-hunting career in China and Tibet, sent Roland E Cooper to Sikkim and Bhutan, and helped finance Reginald Farrer's collecting in China and Burma. Bulley created a new garden at Ness, near Chester, where he could experiment with the newly collected seeds, and many plants grew for the first time in England. Known as Ness Botanic Gardens, these now belong to the University of Liverpool and are open to the public.

Botanical experts across Europe rejoiced at the discoveries and named the new plants. Two genera, *Bulleyia* and *Beesia*, and many species, such as *Primula bulleyana* and *Jasminum beesianum*, were dedicated to Bulley and his nursery,

Bees Ltd, which popularised many of his introductions. Other great gardeners followed Bulley's example of patronage and a whole new range of plants were made available … poppies and gentians, candelabra primulas and rhododendrons galore … a heritage for our enjoyment.

This book tells the story of Bulley's passion for plants, his love of 'out of the way' ones, preferably alpines and hardy plants, and his yearnings and efforts to introduce them to the gardens of Britain. He sought advice and exchanged news with experts at the Royal Botanic Gardens of Kew and Edinburgh, and his letters to them spanned 38 and 25 years respectively. These have been used together with records, Bees' catalogues and other published accounts of his introductions to build up a picture of his achievements. Interviews with his daughter and other people who knew him and his gardens have added the personal touch. The book is a tribute to a remarkable man, of a different era, and it is hoped that the reader will enjoy travelling through time and to distant places with him and his plant hunters.

BRENDA J MCLEAN

Acknowledgements

Ken Hulme inspired this book, when Director of Ness Gardens, and Lois Bulley gave it her blessing. Their enthusiasm has been a spur, their anecdotes a pleasure to pass on. I thank them and everyone, named and unnamed, who has helped in any way.

Memories and stories of Arthur Bulley and his gardens were kindly shared by many people, especially Audrey Hope, Hannah Smith, David Cottrell and Keith Vincent. Background historical information was given by Clyde Binfield, Joan Counihan, Douglas Farnie, Aileen Horobin and Joan Stubbs, whilst Terry Kenwright and Leslie Squire helped with the history of Bees Ltd.

At the Royal Botanic Gardens Kew, Leonora Thompson, Cheryl Piggott, Marilyn Ward and Media Resources helped in the hunt for archives or their reproduction, whilst James Cullen, Colin Will and Debbie White assisted in this at the Royal Botanic Garden, Edinburgh. John Illingworth of Lancaster University helpfully advised me. Further expert help came from staff of the following institutions: the BBC, the Cheshire and Liverpool Record Offices, Marlborough College, The National Botanic Gardens Dublin, National Library of Ireland Dublin, National Museums and Galleries on Merseyside, Natural History Museum, Overseas Missionary Fellowship, Royal Geographical Society, Royal Horticultural Society, and the University of Liverpool. I was privileged to see the family papers of John and Joan Farrer, and I am grateful to all those who gave permission for me to quote from their archives, details of which are in the Notes and References section.

I am indebted to the University of Liverpool for the privileges of a Fellow of the University in the Department of Geography. Sandra Mather skilfully drew all the maps and diagrams, Ian Qualtrough and Suzanne Yee copied many old photographs. I received ready assistance from all the staff of Ness Botanic Gardens, especially Peter Cunnington and Hugh McAllister; and from John Edmondson and Angus Gunn of the Botany Department, Liverpool Museum. The research was eased by the financial support of the Trustees of The Stanley Smith Horticultural Trust and the generous hospitality of the Bennell, Sillitto and Clark families.

In writing the book Anne Dennier was an invaluable mentor, with her patient pruning and improving of numerous drafts, and the suggestion of new ideas. Its remaining deficiencies are my own. Alan Bennell of RBG Edinburgh, Philip Glover, formerly of HMSO, and Valerie Willoughby, formerly at Kew, jointly put their faith in the book. It has been guided to fruition by Grenville Lucas and Sylvia Fitzgerald at Kew and The Stationery

Office team, with Michele Staple as the skilled and sensitive editor. Nearer home I have been helped by Elaine Trott, Joan Yoh and John Hutchinson, and I am immensely grateful to Nancy Kershaw, friends and family for their encouragement, especially Robin, who is always available for advice and has lived lovingly and loyally with it all.

Picture Credits

The author gratefully acknowledges the generosity of the following individuals and institutions in providing illustrations (given as page or plate numbers):

The Board of Trustees of the Royal Botanic Gardens, Kew
pp. 3, 5, 12, 13, 31, 32, 33, 66 (lower), 79, 89 (3), 91, 92, 96 (lower), 105, 113, 120, 124, 131, 133, 136, 146 (top and bottom right), 148.

Plates 1, 2, 3, 15, 16, 20, 21, 22, 23, 24, 27, 28, 29, 30, 31.

Royal Botanic Garden, Edinburgh
pp. 37, 64, 66 (upper), 67, 72, 75, 89 (1, 2), 98, 108.

Plates 11, 18.

The Board of Trustees of the National Museums and Galleries on Merseyside
pp. 25, 27.

The Royal Horticultural Society, the Lindley Library
Plates 14, 32.

Overseas Missionary Fellowship
p. 35.

Liverpool Record Office, Liverpool Libraries and Information Services
pp. 21 (all three pictures), 70.

The University of Liverpool Botanic Garden, and the Department of Special Collections and Archives
pp. 23, 47 (both pictures), 48 (both pictures), 49 (upper), 51 (lower), 53, 73, 74 (both pictures), 76, 87, 88, 102, 114, 117, 130, 157.

Plate 10.

The Liverpool Daily Post and Echo Limited
pp. 54, 158.

K Vincent Frontispiece
J Wissenekker p. 15
Medley & Bird Ltd p. 54
H Smith p. 56
C Grey-Wilson p. 146(bottom left)
A Hope p. 147
Guyse Williams p. 158

P Cunnington Plates 12, 13
J and J Farrer Plate 31
K Hulme Plate 19
J Hutchinson Plates 4, 5, 6, 7, 8, 25
Guan Kaiyun Plate 17
D Leadbetter Plate 9
I Sinclair Plate 26

SOURCES

Botanical illustrations are all by Lilian Snelling except for:
p. 13, Franz Bauer; p. 33, F N Fitch; p. 113, R Farrer.
Plate 1, Mary Wroe; Plate 31 R Farrer.

The maps and diagrams are all drawn by Sandra Mather and compiled by the author. They have the author's copyright.

Cover pictures Flower: Painting of *Meconopsis integrifolia* by Mary Wroe. A K Bulley: photography by Chidley, photographers of Liverpool. B J McLean: photograph by John Hutchinson.

Introduction
Liverpool: the Gateway to the Empire

We know that the commerce and the enterprise of Liverpool are as cosmopolitan as science itself, and that there is no country in the world so remote or so barbarous but that Liverpool men, Liverpool capital, Liverpool enterprise, Liverpool industry have not contrived to find their way (LORD STANLEY, 1861).[1]

What civic pride and confidence! These words of Lord Stanley MP were spoken in 1861, the year Bulley was born into a Liverpool family who prospered as Liverpool trade expanded. Liverpool was then one of the three great maritime commercial centres of the world, with London and New York. The dominant merchandise was cotton, and Bulley's family were brokers at the centre of the cotton trade. They were part of this great entrepôt of commerce where 'Our citizens live, move and have their being in an atmosphere of world trade.'[2] Bulley was nurtured in business in this hub of world trade, he imbibed the atmosphere and epitomised the enterprise of Liverpool merchants at the height of the Empire. Appreciation of this background helps an understanding of Bulley himself.

A great seaport

No longer could there be any claim that Liverpool was merely the 'Creek of the Port of Chester'![3] In the 1720s Daniel Defoe had been impressed by the Liverpool scene: 'The Mersey is a noble harbour, and is able to ride a thousand sail of ships at once … They have made a great wet dock, for laying up their ships.'[4] But during the nineteenth century great changes took place, from sail to steam, wooden ships to iron ships, and 22 docks were built in little over 30 years, housing the largest ships afloat. It was a vibrant, expanding, progressive port, building ships and increasing shipping tonnage and customs revenues as Britain built its Empire.

Fortunes were made and frontiers pushed back. As if pointing the way, statues of Columbus, Cook, Drake, Galileo, Mercator and Raleigh stood on Exchange Flags, the quadrangle created for merchants and brokers to do their business. Liverpool was prominent in transatlantic and tropical trade. There were strong connections with the cotton-growing southern states of America, which are still symbolised in the beautiful ceilings of 19 Abercromby Square (now part of the University of Liverpool). Here an American even had the entrance lobby of his house decorated with the cabbage palmetto tree, *Sabal palmetto*, the state tree of South Carolina.

Soon after the East India Company's monopoly was broken, a Mersey ship was bound for India, and foreign trade expanded in India and the Far East. Liverpool's great steamship lines – *Blue Funnel, White Star, Cunard* and others – took goods and passengers worldwide, and it was said of Liverpool in 1859 that cotton was imported from 'the wide valley of the Mississippi, the banks of the Amazon, the plains of India and the classic soil of Egypt.'[5]

A cotton broker such as Arthur Bulley naturally had a wide network of contacts from consuls to customs men. If cotton could be imported to Liverpool from 'all the cotton growing fields of the earth',[6] why not import seeds of alpine plants from all the alpine areas of the world? And that was exactly Bulley's approach.

There were already many examples of plants and animals being imported through and to Liverpool. The 13th Earl of Derby (1806–1851) at Knowsley Hall obtained living and museum specimens, especially birds and mammals, from all over the world. He had at least 30 agents and several collectors, and interchanged regularly with the London Zoo (founded by one of Bulley's relatives). In Liverpool in Bulley's day, an alderman traded monkeys and parrots, and a zoological park at Mossley Hill rivalled London and Hamburg in the importation and distribution of exotic animals. The Liverpool Horticultural Company advertised an immense stock of orchids. But a venture most in line with the aspirations of Arthur Bulley was the early-nineteenth-century Liverpool Botanic Garden.

The fleeting fame of the Liverpool Botanic Garden

In the development of the Empire, botanic gardens were laid out in virtually all the colonies, beginning with St Vincent in the mid-eighteenth century. The primary purpose of this network was not for collecting rare or curious plants, but for growing and distributing economically useful plants, to promote the prosperity of the Empire and ultimately to benefit the commerce of Britain. The botanic gardens were unique foci for the import and export, collection and distribution of plants and seeds between Britain and the colonies. The network helped in the spread of important commercial crops: cinchona (for quinine) from the Andes, tea from China and rubber from Brazil. Kew became the key link in the system, but with Liverpool's merchant wealth and foreign connections it too was ideally placed to take part.

The Liverpool Botanic Garden was the brainchild of William Roscoe (1753–1831), one of Liverpool's most distinguished citizens. Money was raised by subscriptions and shares and, in May 1802, a 10-acre (4-ha) botanic garden was established on a ridge overlooking the town (next to the present university campus). It was the first in the world to be developed by public subscription to a private society, the number of members or proprietors being limited to 300 (gentlemen only, 'Ladies may enter with Proprietors').[7]

The garden soon became famous, in the foremost rank of European gardens. Pioneering experiments on growing ferns from spores accompanied the introduction of new plants. A conservatory was built, 240 feet (73 m) long, one of the biggest in the country at that time. It had five sections at different temperatures, to grow seeds and plants from many parts of the world. Some were brought back by masters of ships, others were obtained through botanic gardens, private gardens and nurseries, while some were sent by plant collectors. Some species were to flower in the garden for the first time outside their native habitat, and a new genus of American plants, *Shepherdia*, was named after the curator of the garden, John Shepherd.

The conservatory of Liverpool's first botanic garden, opened in 1803.

The traffic was not all one way: in 1824 the Liverpool garden sent over a thousand English fruit trees to Calcutta to see if they could be naturalised in parts of Hindustan and Nepal. A vast number of rare and beautiful plants were also given to the Imperial Botanic Garden at St Petersburg. In return in 1825 the Liverpool Botanic Garden received the treasured *Flora Rossica*, published in the reign of Catherine the Great. Czar Alexander was so pleased with his plants that the curator, John Shepherd, was presented with a diamond ring.

Meanwhile, Roscoe continued his own botanical studies on the ginger family, and Sir James E Smith, founder and President of the Linnean Society of London, dedicated his classical work *Exotic Botany* to him. In it was mentioned *Roscoea purpurea* Sm., a new genus named in honour of Roscoe, and found flowering, in 1802, in the mountains of Nepal. Happily, over one hundred years later, one of Bulley's collectors was to find another species, *Roscoea humeana* (Plate 19), in western China, so increasing our knowledge of the genus, and its Liverpool associations.

By the time Bulley was born, the Liverpool Botanic Garden was, sadly, past its heyday. It had been moved out of town, to Edge Lane, to avoid the spread of housing and smoke pollution. It had been taken over as municipal gardens, and by 1896 it was merely the production site for bedding and municipal display plants. There were ornamental beds with fine scroll designs, ideal for inspection by visiting dignitaries such as the Sultan of Zanzibar, or for garden parties, such as the one on Queen Victoria's Diamond Jubilee day when over

2000 people were invited to the gardens. But one of Roscoe's first and basic aims had gone: scientific enquiry. Bulley was scathing about it: 'The Chairman … and the rest of the honourable committee have a combined knowledge of gardening altogether below a guinea pig's.'[8] He hoped to sneak in reforms when he could, but the best thing for him to do was to strike out on his own in the introduction of new garden plants. He sought stimulus and information elsewhere, from the Royal Botanic Gardens at Edinburgh and Kew, and the Royal Horticultural Society. By the 1890s local horticultural societies were formed in almost every provincial town, and botanical and horticultural novelties attracted attention from scientists and gardeners. Yet there were temperate areas of the world still unexplored for alpine and hardy plants. Bulley saw the potential market and took this opportunity.

Bulley made full use of the imperial network of botanical gardens and stations. They were listed in the *Kew Bulletin* from 1889, giving their personnel and addresses, and in the 1890s he followed the course of the first curator of the Liverpool Botanic Garden, and exchanged seed with gardens from Calcutta to St Petersburg.

News and views from afar

For Liverpool's men of commerce, exploration had the scent of new possibilities for trade; for Bulley it also meant plants! He was in a milieu where news of one could help the other, and he was never slow to use his contacts. Moreover, he could combine the news he received from many different quarters, from visitors to the city and papers in the Exchange newsroom, correspondence from customs officers and missionaries, and information from books and learned journals which were readily available in the libraries of Liverpool.

Dr David Livingstone, the celebrated explorer and missionary in Africa, visited Liverpool in 1857. He addressed a meeting of merchants and others in the Cotton Salesroom, and across the Mersey in Birkenhead, a contract was agreed to build ship 225, the *Ma-Robert*, a paddle-steamer, for his navigation of the Zambezi river. Henry Stanley, who was later sent to find Livingstone, came to be feted at a banquet in the Town Hall, and in 1890, he delivered a lecture in St George's Hall. But interest in the 'scramble for Africa' was also accompanied by mercantile pressure on the government for more trade with China. Yunnan was perceived as the El Dorado of optimistic traders, and for Bulley during the 1890s, more news was also coming in of the beautiful plants of Yunnan, and the possibilities of new garden plants.

The Chambers of Commerce of Manchester and Liverpool were eager to expand their market for manufactured goods, especially cotton textiles, and China's enormous population seemed to offer unlimited possibilities. In 1851 the quickest return sailing by clipper to China from Liverpool was 7 months and 7 days, but with the coming of steamships, the opening of the Suez Canal and telegraphic communication, the obstacle of distance was gradually overcome. The problems of penetration of the vast interior were more intractable. In 1858 a treaty had given official concessions for British subjects to travel for pleasure or trade to all parts of the interior, but there was strife within China and rebellion against the decadent Manchu dynasty. There were problems of language, travel, rights of residence, and a strong anti-foreign feeling which put their lives at risk. However, the immense resources and markets of inland China continued to be a focus of exploration and jealous international competition.

From the 1840s, the textile lobby in England was keen on a short, direct, overland route from the port of Rangoon to Bhamo in upper Burma and into Yunnan, south-west China. This would save on ocean freight and avoid much longer overland routes from Chinese ports. Information was sought on possible alternative routes by rail, road and river; early consular agents made enormous journeys through uncharted territory of south-western China in the 1880s. Alexander Hosie, for example, travelled over 5000 miles, mostly on foot and horseback, in the years 1882–4, and sent despatches to both Houses of Parliament, addressed a special meeting of the Manchester Chamber of Commerce, and wrote a book on his travels, which Bulley read with eager enthusiasm.[9] Hosie warned of the difficulties of communications – even along a proposed major (and ancient) trade route from Bhamo: 'a footpath only passable by mules and pack-coolies, and on which mounted men are often compelled to dismount and lead their animals a great part of the way.' But there was still a thirst for more knowledge of the country and its resources.

In the 1890s, the Royal Geographical Society published reports and sketch maps resulting from the travels of French and English explorers, and both countries sent out commercial missions to Yunnan, one from Lyons in 1895–7 and one from the Blackburn Chamber of Commerce in 1896–7. But the Blackburn report in many ways showed bleak commercial prospects, finding no right to manufacture, or engage in mining or planting, and at the same time facing strong competition for a limited market of foreign cottons.[10] In complete contrast, the reports on the plants of the region were mouth-watering to botanists and horticulturalists alike!

Augustine Henry (1857–1930)

The *Kew Bulletin* of the 1890s reported botanical explorations in different parts of the Himalayas, from Kashmir and Karakoram to Sikkim and Tibet. Furthermore, it was possible to hear first-hand about the great journey of Mr and Mrs St George Littledale across Tibet, when it was recounted at the British Association in Liverpool in 1896. (They saw some species of *Meconopsis*, a genus which Bulley loved.) From Yunnan itself came news of the plant discoveries of French missionaries; they were finding plants of the greatest garden importance, but more seed was needed to try and grow them in Europe. In the closing years of the nineteenth century, Yunnan beckoned Bulley as two consulates were opened in the south-west, and he knew customs officers at both of them! They sent him seed, and he had up-to-date information on the opening of the direct, overland route to Yunnan – a route which was to be used many times by his collectors. In 1899 his friend and customs officer, Augustine Henry, wrote from Yunnan issuing the ultimate challenge which Bulley could not resist: 'Until the great region Northeast, as it were, of the Himalayas is explored, people will have no idea of the richness of the world in beautiful plants.'[11]

A new gateway was opening, and from his experience Bulley had sufficient knowledge to realise the potential beyond. He grasped the opportunity as soon as he could, and ushered in a golden age of twentieth-century plant collecting in one of the richest areas in the world.

Part I

A Flowering Passion

1

Bulley's Background: Free-thinking Victorians

'Tenax propositi' (tenacious of purpose) — BULLEY FAMILY MOTTO

Arthur K Bulley was born in 1861 when the port of Liverpool was booming. He was born and brought up in New Brighton, a new suburb across the River Mersey. The family villa looked out to sea, to the busy shipping scene. Sailing and steamships were bound for far-flung places, and the family's horizons stretched far beyond the local shores.

Earlier in the nineteenth century, the Bulleys' forebears had already spread far across the globe. His mother's cousin, Sir Stamford Raffles, was hoisting the British flag in Singapore; his father's cousin, Samuel Bulley, was establishing family commercial links in the cotton-growing area of Charleston, South Carolina. Other relatives were in even more remote places, with the London Missionary Society.

We will take a peep into Arthur Bulley's stimulating and varied family background to uncover the different strands interwoven in this energetic and unconventional man. His lively mind encompassed many interests, and stretched far across the oceans, too, in his work and hobbies, in commercial contacts and in his search for new garden plants.

Two families meet in Liverpool

The family links with Liverpool began when both of Arthur Bulley's grandfathers, Thomas Bulley and Thomas Raffles, came to the rapidly expanding port early in the nineteenth century, and met through the Congregational Chapel. They settled and thrived in the town, and their families flourished, shared a love of travel, and a pioneering, enterprising spirit.

The Bulleys were originally farmers, on the Devon/Dorset border, but were drawn to the sea and became traders with Newfoundland. Arthur Bulley's paternal grandfather, Thomas Bulley (1780–1853), was a sea captain trading from Teignmouth until the wars with France brought danger in the English Channel at the beginning of the nineteenth century. Ships were burned, sailors captured and imprisoned. Thomas and his brother-in-law, John Job, decided to move to the safer port of Liverpool — war refugees from Devon.

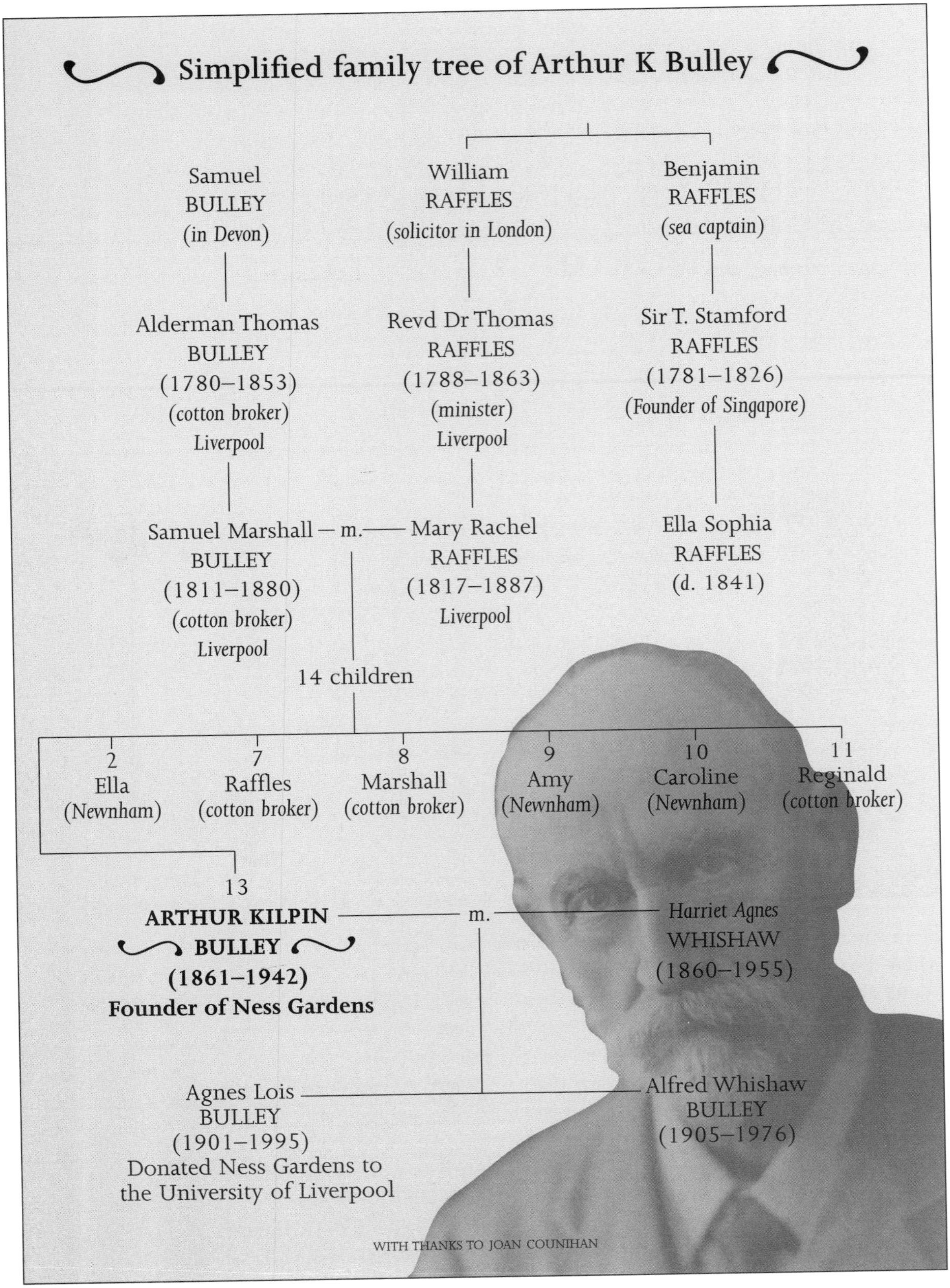

Simplified family tree of Arthur K Bulley

Samuel BULLEY (in Devon)	William RAFFLES (solicitor in London)	Benjamin RAFFLES (sea captain)

Alderman Thomas BULLEY (1780–1853) (cotton broker) Liverpool	Revd Dr Thomas RAFFLES (1788–1863) (minister) Liverpool	Sir T. Stamford RAFFLES (1781–1826) (Founder of Singapore)

Samuel Marshall — m.—— Mary Rachel
BULLEY   RAFFLES
(1811–1880)   (1817–1887)
(cotton broker)   Liverpool
Liverpool

Ella Sophia
RAFFLES
(d. 1841)

14 children

2 Ella (Newnham)	7 Raffles (cotton broker)	8 Marshall (cotton broker)	9 Amy (Newnham)	10 Caroline (Newnham)	11 Reginald (cotton broker)

13
ARTHUR KILPIN BULLEY ———— m. ———— Harriet Agnes
BULLEY   WHISHAW
(1861–1942)   (1860–1955)
Founder of Ness Gardens

Agnes Lois   Alfred Whishaw
BULLEY   BULLEY
(1901–1995)   (1905–1976)
Donated Ness Gardens to
the University of Liverpool

WITH THANKS TO JOAN COUNIHAN

By 1810, before steam boats were on the River Mersey, they were merchants in the Counting House at Salthouse Dock, Liverpool. Then Thomas Bulley joined the expanding and lucrative cotton trade with the southern states of the USA. He and his son, Samuel Marshall Bulley (1811–1880), registered as cotton brokers in Liverpool. Samuel Marshall Bulley later established his own family firm of cotton brokers, S M Bulley and Son, in which three of his sons, including Arthur Bulley, eventually became partners. So Arthur Bulley was the third generation of Bulleys in commerce in Liverpool and involved in transatlantic trade. He seemed to inherit a business instinct and it was his success in business which enabled him to indulge in financing plant hunters across the globe, and to buy land on which to grow the new introductions.

In contrast, the Raffles family originally came from Beverley, east Yorkshire, where an ancestor, John Raffles, was mayor in 1538. Arthur Bulley's maternal grandfather, Thomas Raffles (1788–1863) was born in London, the son of a solicitor. He was a great collector of books, curios and autographs and he was ordained in London in 1809. He did not seek to come to Liverpool, but came at the invitation of the Congregational Chapel where Thomas Bulley was a deacon. They had heard of the power of Raffles' preaching, and they invited him to 'supply the pulpit', hoping that he would replace their late minister and successfully fill their new chapel which was planned to hold 2000 people. What a challenge for a young man of only 23 years!

Thomas Raffles accepted the appointment, the new chapel in Great George Street was built and it was soon filled with wealthy and influential people who

The Levee, New Orleans, 1884. The Bulleys' wealth was founded on American cotton, and A K Bulley was a member of the New Orleans Cotton Exchange.

then lived in this prosperous, middle-class area. He was a popular, genial and witty man, and 'Raffles of Liverpool' became a natural civic leader, widely known and loved.

He was a minister in Liverpool for 49 years, during which the Bulleys were great family friends. The men would meet in the Athenaeum and at civic functions. (Thomas Bulley became one of Liverpool's first aldermen.) The families worshipped at the same chapel and enjoyed family gatherings together. In 1838 they were united through marriage, when the Raffles' only daughter, Mary Rachel Raffles, married the Bulleys' only surviving son, Samuel Marshall Bulley. Her father performed the ceremony at Great George Street Chapel. The young couple lived near the Raffles' home in Edge Hill, and had several children there, before they moved out to New Brighton, where Arthur Bulley was born. When Revd Dr Thomas Raffles died in 1863, Arthur Bulley

Sir T Stamford Raffles
(1781–1826)

was only two years old, but his two eldest brothers, then aged 15 and 13 years, were considered old enough to walk in the funeral procession. It must have been an occasion which they vividly remembered, for it was reported that the funeral procession was five miles long, and that the throng of people around the chapel would have filled 'fifty such chapels, spacious though it be'.[1]

Sir Stamford Raffles

The most famous member of the Raffles family was Sir T Stamford Raffles (1781–1826), who founded Singapore. The family was very fond and proud of him. He was first cousin and close friend of Revd Dr Thomas Raffles (Arthur Bulley's grandfather) and the two men corresponded at great length. In 1819, when Stamford Raffles was at sea, he wrote 'tell your little ones that they have an uncle who does not forget them.'[2]

In 1817 they had holidayed together, touring Europe by carriage in a family party, long before there were any Cook's tours. Indeed, Revd Dr Thomas Raffles made detailed notes of the journey, and his subsequent book, *Tour on the Continent*, went through five editions in England and was widely read in America.

Sir T Stamford Raffles was born at sea, off Jamaica, his father being a captain in the West Indies trade. He, himself, went to south-east Asia with the East India Company. He realised the potential trading importance of Singapore, then almost an uninhabited island, and was acclaimed for contributing to the extension of the Empire and its commerce. He was also a plant collector, and sent some collections to his friend Sir Joseph Banks. So Arthur Bulley was not the first member of the family to collect plants and to have some named after him; he once said that plant collecting was in his blood … and it was!

When Raffles was Governor of Sumatra he enjoyed exploring the island, travelling on foot through thick forest. He was rewarded in May 1818 by finding an extraordinary, unknown and enormous flower, a jungle parasite measuring a metre across. It was later named *Rafflesia arnoldii*, in memory of his accompanying botanist, Dr Joseph Arnold, who died soon afterwards.[3] As it is one of the world's largest and rarest flowers, efforts are now being made to try and protect it from extinction.[4]

Sir Stamford Raffles was a founder and first President of the Zoological Society in London. In 1825 he wrote to his cousin, Revd Dr Thomas Raffles, that he was interested in establishing 'a Society for the introduction of living animals',[5] and his collection of Sumatran animals formed the nucleus of Regent's Park Zoo. One of the primary aims was the introduction of new breeds or varieties of animals from every part of the globe, with a view to their possible use

Rafflesia arnoldii, one of the world's largest flowers, discovered in Sumatra by Sir T Stamford Raffles in 1818.

or domestication, as well as a source of interest and gratification. This is similar to the later aim of Arthur Bulley who wished to introduce new hardy and alpine plants for possible use in our gardens.

In an age of heroes, Arthur Bulley had one in the family. Sadly, though, all Stamford Raffles' children died; his last surviving child, Ella Sophia, died before she was 20, in 1841. In her memory, the next child born to Mary Bulley (née Raffles) was named Ella Sophia – an elder and influential sister of Arthur Bulley. Arthur's eldest brother and sister also had the middle name of Raffles, and the eldest brother was always called by that name.

The Bulley and Raffles families combined many talents in the marriage of Samuel Marshall Bulley and Mary Rachel Raffles. It is not surprising that the progeny of this marriage included some very able, enterprising and energetic people – including Arthur Kilpin Bulley.

Childhood in New Brighton

In the mid-1840s Mr and Mrs S M Bulley moved to New Brighton with their young family. The cotton trade was booming, so they could launch out as pioneers of this new, exclusive and promising seaside resort, away from smokey Liverpool and its disease-ridden, smelly slums. In 1830 a retired Liverpool merchant had bought 170 acres (69 ha) of sandhills and heathland and had begun laying out roads on the sandstone cliffs so that splendid villas, with their own gardens, provided breath-taking, panoramic views across Liverpool Bay, and out to the Irish Sea. It was advertised as an 'attractive and fashionable Watering Place', and steam ferries and horse-drawn cabs enabled prosperous middle-class people to escape across the Mersey to their

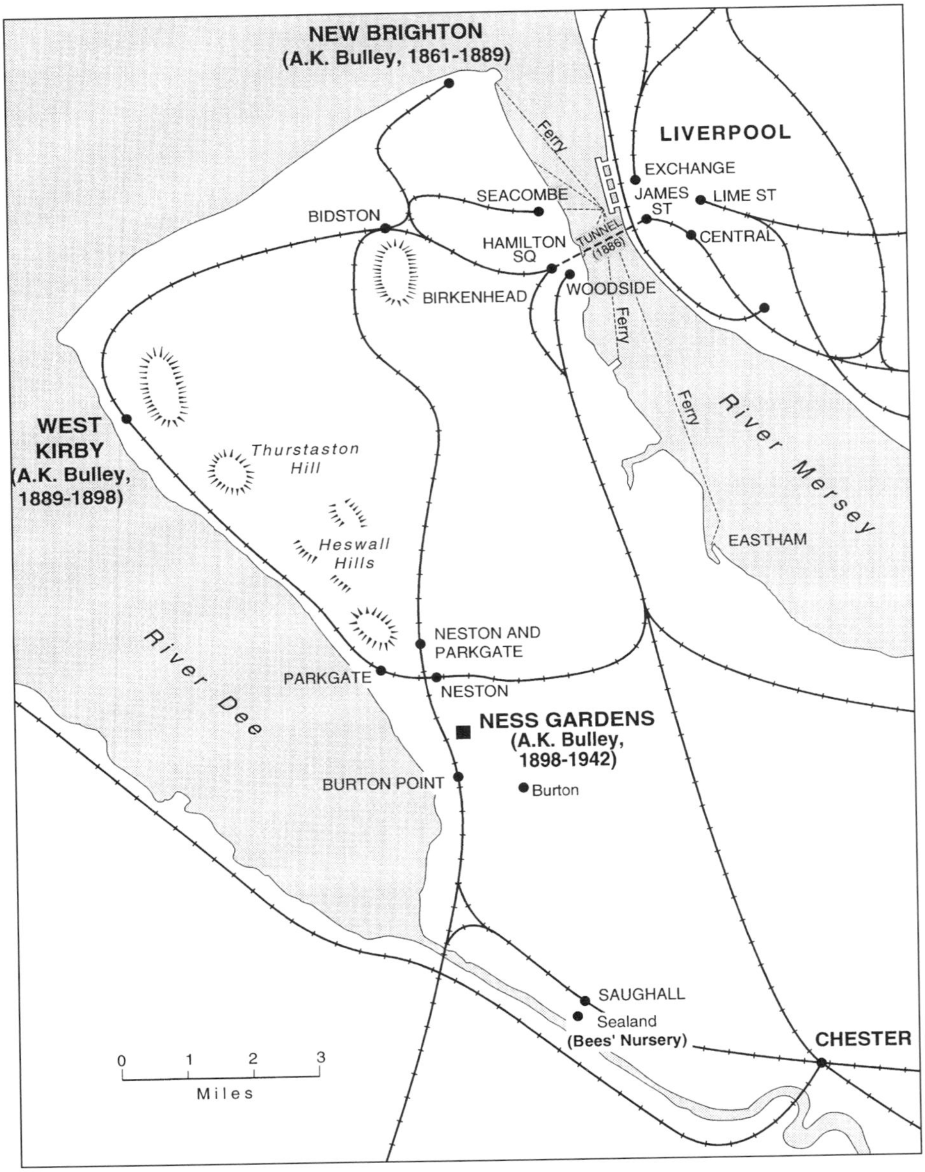

NEW BRIGHTON
(A.K. Bulley, 1861-1889)

LIVERPOOL

EXCHANGE
SEACOMBE
JAMES ST
LIME ST
HAMILTON SQ
TUNNEL (1886)
CENTRAL
BIDSTON
WOODSIDE
BIRKENHEAD
Ferry
River Mersey

WEST KIRBY
(A.K. Bulley, 1889-1898)

Thurstaston Hill

Heswall Hills

EASTHAM

NESTON AND PARKGATE

PARKGATE
NESTON

River Dee

NESS GARDENS
(A.K. Bulley, 1898-1942)

BURTON POINT
Burton

SAUGHALL
Sealand
(Bees' Nursery)

CHESTER

0   1   2   3
Miles

Wirral Railways and A K Bulley. He moved house as the network expanded.

comfortable homes and plenty of fresh air. In those days there was a lovely sandy beach, and Mrs Bulley's father, Revd Dr Raffles, had already bought a shoreline villa which he named 'Stamford' in memory of his distinguished cousin. This was his holiday home, but Mr and Mrs S M Bulley moved to New Brighton permanently.

They moved to Montpellier Crescent before half the plots of land were built on, and they lived for 20 years in Montpellier Lodge, Montpellier Crescent, with a cliff-top view overlooking the multitude of ships sailing in and out of the Mersey estuary. This was where Bulley was born. He was their thirteenth child. Indeed, they reared 14 fit and healthy children who all lived to marry, in great contrast to the poverty and child mortality of Liverpool slums, where mortality rates then were among the highest in England. So Arthur Bulley was privileged to grow up in this large, stimulating, stable and prosperous family.

The year Arthur Bulley was born there was a household of 22 people: 14 members of the family, a governess and seven servants. As was the custom, each of the boys was given a middle, family name, and Arthur's was Kilpin after a great uncle, Revd Samuel Kilpin (1774–1830), whom the family had looked up to as a saintly, enterprising Baptist minister who housed refugee women and orphans in Exeter in the Napoleonic Wars.

Bulley's parents lived in this crescent for the rest of their lives, but when Arthur was five years old they all moved into a new, detached villa which they called 'The Gables'. When he was ten years old, there were still seven children at home, and seven servants — a waitress, cook, two nurses, two housemaids and one kitchen maid. Arthur Bulley lived in this house as a young cotton salesman playing rugby in the local club, and it was his home base for over 20 years, until after his widowed mother died in 1887.

'The Gables', Montpellier Crescent, New Brighton. This was Arthur Bulley's home for over 20 years. The family coat of arms is on the porch.

The family attended the Independent Chapel in Liscard, and over a period of 75 years, 19 members of the immediate family became members of that chapel. Imagine the shock and sadness in the family when two of the sons, Samuel Marshall and Arthur Kilpin, later became agnostic. Their father, Samuel Marshall Bulley, was a staunch Nonconformist and believed in a regular family pattern of weekly chapel attendance and daily morning prayers, a moral upbringing, and a beating if a child deserved it. He was a strong and forceful character who knew his mind and spoke it. At chapel he resigned from being deacon when there was a difference of opinion. He was a man of high ideals and great resolve, and he decided that his family should have a coat of arms depicting a rampant bull's head with the motto *Tenax propositi* (tenacious of purpose) taken from one of Horace's 'Roman' odes. (The appropriate part declares that man should be just, never crooked and always determined.) The shield was on his shaving mug, and also above the porch of their home, as if to remind all who entered in.

The children had a strict but happy, stimulating childhood. They enjoyed life. There was a popular sandy beach at New Brighton in Victorian times, and Liverpool people flocked there to enjoy the delights of the new resort: swings and donkeys, bathing huts and photographers' tents. The Bulley children, girls and boys, could play hockey together on the beach, when it would have been frowned upon elsewhere. At home there was music-making, plenty of fun, verve and spirited company, and a healthy exchange of ideas. Enterprise and independent spirit were encouraged. As the children grew up, many of them, including Arthur, showed tremendous initiative, imagination and drive, combined with a strong social conscience. They held contrasting views on religion, politics and the role of women in society, but there was also a basic acceptance of this range of opinion, and enough common interests and loyalty to keep the family together.

Arthur Bulley benefited from the social contacts which his elder brothers and sisters brought into the family, including a childhood friend who later became his wife. This charming girl was Harriet Whishaw, whom the family always called 'Hetty'. Her father was a widower and clergyman and had married one of Arthur's elder sisters. They lived round the corner in New Brighton and there is a delightful story of an early encounter between the two children one teatime. In those strict Victorian days, the children were only allowed either butter or jam on their toast, but not both. Arthur revealed his cunning and wily ways which were to help him in later life: he carefully split the toast, buttered it and put it together again so that the toast looked bare. He then asked 'Can I have some jam?' Hetty was seated opposite, her eyes growing rounder with incredulity at this audacious act, whereupon he winked at her![6]

Education

The first six children were girls, and only four of the 14 children were boys. The elder children were educated at home with an excellent governess; the younger ones went to boarding school, girls going to Laleham School, Clapham, where there was a gifted and dedicated teacher, Hannah Pipe, at a time when the private schools for girls were often awful. Clearly their parents valued a good and liberal education, and this led to some stunning results.

At the age of 15, Ella resolved not to be hemmed in by Victorian conventions. In secret code she wrote in her diary, 'I dwell under the accursed thraldom of womanhood. Could I but burst these bonds asunder.'[7] And she did. She vowed to read and learn as much as she could, mastered five languages and met leading figures in women's education: Miss Clough, Miss Beale and Miss Buss.

In the early 1870s, Ella and two of her sisters, Amy and Caroline, pioneered women's higher education at Cambridge University. Ella was one of the original five students of Newnham College, and Amy was one of the first two women to take the Moral Sciences Tripos, gaining a first class. The Bulley sisters were to challenge many social norms as they invaded the bastion of a man's world of learning; they were also Nonconformists in a Church of England community. They had to put up with names like 'forward minxes', and being chaperoned to lectures and not being allowed to play outdoor games or go cycling. But they were as determined as their father! They encouraged other women in higher education and wrote books and articles on many subjects. Ella wrote a classic book on Norman castles, and was awarded an honorary MA degree by Manchester University for her archaeological studies. Forceful Amy worked for women's suffrage and trade unions, and when Arthur Bulley was asked, later in life, what had made him so keen on women's suffrage, he replied that it was because he had so many bossy sisters!

When Arthur Bulley was born his eldest sister was already married, and Ella, 20 years his senior, was expected to help look after the younger children, despite her yearnings to study. She had her hands full: there were still seven children aged 12 years and younger – and one more babe to come. However, when Arthur was seven years old, boarding school began. He went to Mostyn House School at Parkgate, near Chester, where he was a near contemporary of Wilfred Grenfell of Labrador fame. He won a prize and his future studies must have looked promising.

At 13 Bulley went to Marlborough. He was on the 'classical side' and studied Latin, Greek and French – all of which were useful later in his ready grasp of plant names and his European travels. But he hated being at Marlborough and despite his intelligence he was not a high-flyer or fired by the opportunities at the school. Curiously, his name does not even appear on the list of members of the flourishing Natural History Society which the Revd W Keble Martin was to join a few years later. Bulley was used to a freeflow of ideas and expression at home. Did he find school too constraining, like a strait-jacket, being too much of an individualist for that environment?

Manhood

In marked contrast to the girls, no boys went to university; they were expected to go into their father's cotton firm straight from school, and three of the boys became senior partners in S M Bulley and Son. For Arthur Bulley this was no handicap, for he thrived in business. He was a great opportunist, with the confidence to take risks and back his own judgement. As a cotton broker he was at the centre of the cotton trade, doing business on the Liverpool Cotton Exchange, and after the First World War he rethought his business and also became a merchant, hiring warehouses along canals to hoard cotton until the market was more favourable. Great profits could be made, and it is rumoured locally that Bulley once made a profit of £120,000 on a consignment of cotton sold on the high seas. But prices could also come tumbling down and there were times when very little money was coming in at all. It was a world of speculation and outwitting the next man, but Bulley was highly competitive, as will be seen in his determination to be the first to introduce some alpine species to Britain, and to succeed at horticultural shows.

He also diversified his business investments with great success. He saw the commercial value of the nursery trade and began his own nursery in 1904. This expanded as Bees Ltd, and seeds were sold on the high street, through Woolworths, for 50 years. His great success later in life came in investments in East Africa. He set up his nephew, J R Cox, in business, and J R Cox & Co. Ltd came to own Motormart and Exchange. Motormart operated throughout East Africa, and held the franchises of General Motors, Massey Harris Ferguson and Firestone Tyre. His daughter also recounts that in March 1929, Bulley returned from one of his globe-trotting trips to find that, although his business was booming, it had taken out enormous bank loans, and he insisted, against all advice, that the stocks and shares be sold and the banks paid off. 'Then, out of the blue, within a few weeks, came the 1929 crash when the value of stocks and shares were halved in a night. As it fell out, my father never did a shrewder thing.'[8]

Bulley's marriage to Harriet Whishaw was a deep source of happiness, a stable and reassuring partnership. Because of his agnosticism they were married in a registry office in Birkenhead; it was 21 April 1890 and they were both 29 years old. In some ways they were extremely different. He was over 6 feet (1.8 m) tall and she was only 5 feet 1 inch (1.55 m). He was agnostic, she was deeply religious. He was more the intellectual, she loved to be involved with people. They understood and complemented each other, and she supported him in his political activities and in running the garden. They shared a sense of fun and social concern, a love of nature and outdoor pursuits. Their hospitality meant sharing their home and their holidays, and their generosity extended to anyone they met in distress or need, from food for striking miners to a bath for a filthy thief ...

Riversdale House, Riversdale Road, West Kirby was their first home together, close to the recently opened railway link to Liverpool, yet with open country and shore to explore and a soot-free environment for gardening. Five years later they moved up the hill to a sandstone house, 'Claremont', on Darmonds Green, with a commanding view out to Hilbre Island and the sea, until they moved, in 1898, to Mickwell Brow, Ness, not far from where Bulley first went to school. Their lives blossomed at Ness. In 1901, when Harriet was 40, their first child, Agnes Lois, was born, and four years later their son, Alfred. As the children grew, so the garden flourished and the Bulleys lived there happily for the rest of their lives.

Bulley's Liverpool cotton business kept him home-based until his retirement, but it also gave him the finance and leisure to do many things. He enjoyed a variety of activities, and challenges excited him. He taught himself German and Esperanto, joined learned societies, read novels and travel books, floras and philosophical works. He believed strongly that everyone should have a hobby, and he had several! He loved music and sang German and English Lieder. He was a very keen chess player. He entered politics with gusto, and he loved striding over the hills. But his abiding joy in adult life was his garden and his fascination with alpine plants.

Love of flowers

It seems likely that Arthur Bulley first learned his love of flowers as a child. His elder sister, Ella, who helped to bring him up, certainly encouraged her own children to collect ferns and butterflies, and to gather lots of anemones on beautiful woodland walks. In those different days over a hundred years ago, it didn't seem a crime to pick plants – rather, it showed appreciation of God's creation. Ella married a minister, and in their Congregational church they held flower services and he preached on 'wild flowers' and on 'worms and insects as God's gardeners'. Ella's husband was so keen on gardening that at one stage he was concerned that it might be competing too much with his church duties as a minister!

In the Bulley family there were other keen gardeners building alpine rockeries and trying out different plants. One elder brother, Marshall, lived graciously in grounds going down to the River Mersey, but he retired in his early forties and had a handsome house built in 36 acres (14.5 ha) of land at West Down, Hindhead, Surrey. He was so keen that he sent a photograph to the *Gardeners' Chronicle* of *Ptilotrichum spinosum* (syn. *Alyssum spinosum*) growing unusually large on his rockery,[9] followed by another article with a photograph of plants in his alpine house.[10] His eldest brother, Raffles, had a 2.5-acre (1-ha) garden, and later wrote an enthusiastic and knowledgeable article in the *Gardeners' Chronicle*, in praise of the alpine house. He had one which was 30 feet (9 m) long and obviously gave him hours of pleasure. So when Arthur Bulley wanted to have a larger garden and start a plant and seed nursery, he had plenty of support. These two brothers also became members of the RHS and Raffles contributed £60 to the memorial volume of the Empire Exhibition of 1912, where Bees Ltd was exhibiting. There was a common bond in the love of gardening, and a dedication which the eldest brother showed in his article: 'No success will be achieved without constant thought, but to the real lover of a garden that is only an enhancement of the pleasure.'[11]

The extended family

As the 14 children married into other large families, the extended family became enormous. Most of the 14 had two to four children of their own, producing a huge cousinage, and the Wirral was 'thick with Bulleys'.[12] Intermarriage occurred between cousins and between generations, forming a complex web of relationships, often within the same commercial-social-religious circle.[13] For example, the Bulleys were long-standing friends of the Armitages, cotton spinners of Manchester; both families were Nonconformists, their children knew each other through joint family gatherings, school, university or business and Congregational links. There were two marriages between their children within two years, and also in the next generation.

In the days of no television or radio, family gatherings were valued for mutual entertainment and an exchange of news and views, and these two families met at Christmas in New Brighton and for the New Year in Altrincham. When Arthur Bulley's brother, Raffles, was the host in New Brighton, his villa overflowed with family, laughter and merriment, and summer family picnics might involve over 30 members of all ages travelling up to the Lake District.

As Arthur Bulley's brothers and sisters married, new interests and skills were brought into the family. Among the girls, three married clerics, two married academics (one a lecturer in classics, the other, Professor John Cox, was the Cambridge physicist who helped Rutherford split the atom) and one married a solicitor. Three of the children settled in America, strengthening the family ties there, and in the wider family there were relatives in Canada and Tasmania, interests in South African gold mines, and visits to Brazil and Argentina, Australia and the Middle East.

Harriet Whishaw's father was a charming and learned man, born in St Petersburg and fluent in several languages. He had been a teacher and a canon of Gloucester Cathedral before being chaplain to the Institution for the Blind in Liverpool. On her mother's side of the family, Harriet was cousin to Dr Edward Wilson, a close friend of Captain R F Scott of the Antarctic. When, in 1912, Wilson and Scott undertook their tragic return from the South Pole, the Bulleys must have felt closely involved. It was Wilson who insisted that they should haul their geological specimens as far as they could go in the extreme conditions. When their dead bodies were found, Scott's arm was flung across Wilson, and 16 kg weight of geological specimens were on their sledge. The Siberian dogs they had used were the gifts of schools, including Laleham School, which Amy and Caroline Bulley had attended.

Socialist ideals

Bulley claimed that when he was at Marlborough, 'The school was a hot-bed of conservatism and clericalism, and I emerged a socialist and an agnostic.'[14] He knew and loathed the evils and inequalities of class-ridden cities such as Liverpool. Masses of people lived in unhealthy, sordid slums close to the prosperous Exchange and he longed to change things for the better. He believed that political reform was required. He joined the Fabians, the first socialist society in Britain, founded in 1884 and earnestly keen for social change. Their first tract was headed 'Why are the Many Poor?'

In 1897 Bulley jokingly warned an intending visitor about his political leanings. 'I think you will do well to equip yourself with suitable firearms and bludgeons, for there is evidently going to be a row. You hold Socialism damnable, well, I am a Socialist. As I say that, I recognise the smack of pleasurable defiance in it.' He even went on to say, 'I think Individualism is the direct offspring of the devil … If I must label myself I am a Socialist rather than an Individualist, but all I really mean is that I think the text of the one "Every man for himself and devil take the hindmost", is a poor thing by the text of the other "Every man for himself and his brother".'[15]

In 1905 he began a notebook in which the opening quotation was from Bacon: 'Men ought to know that in the theatre of life it is only for God and angels to be spectators.' Bulley himself could no longer be a spectator and his political campaigns in Liverpool began.

Bulley's socialist leanings were an oddity at the Cotton Exchange: a publication of 1908 described him as a 'pronounced Socialist, and does a good deal of speaking in connection with that body of idealistic theorists. He is the sole representative on the Exchange, we believe, of the doctrines of Agnosticism and Socialism.'[16]

This did not worry Bulley. Eventually he fought for Labour in three municipal elections from 1910 to 1912, in a very poor area of Liverpool, where the working classes were mainly Conservative – and he was unsuccessful. Nor was he daunted by the fleas which he inevitably collected at political meetings. In 1910 he was even a Women's Suffrage candidate in Rossendale, Lancashire; he lost, but maintained his long-term vision. After all, the motto of the Liverpool and District Independent Labour Party, of which he became treasurer, was 'They conquer who believe they can' (Virgil). This was Bulley's fundamental outlook.

Bulley's unconventionality was perceived as eccentricity by the many establishment figures in Liverpool and the Royal Horticultural Society in London. He did not dress 'properly', having no starched shirts or collars, no creases in his trousers. He once wore a deerstalker among the top hats and bowlers on the Cotton Flags, and when wearing his customary comfy, shabby hat, a businessman on the ferry expostulated, 'If I see that hat again, Bulley, I'll throw it in the river!'[17] In eating habits in the middle of the day, he also stood out from his business colleagues. He was not a member of the Athenaeum, but went there to talk business, and while others wined and dined he had water with a beef or cheese sandwich. This was so regular that when the steward

(*Above*) Cartoon of *A K Bulley*, 1908. *Note the socialist document in his pocket.*

(*Far left*) *A K Bulley was an unsuccessful Women's Suffrage candidate at Rossendale, Lancashire in 1910.*

(*Left*) *A K Bulley tried for election to Liverpool City Council, but never succeeded.*

ROSSENDALE ELECTION, 1910.

COPY OF LETTER TO
WOMEN'S SUFFRAGE CANDIDATE.

Liverpool Labour Representation Committee
Sec: ARTHUR W. SHORT.   Affiliated to the National Labour Party.

8, Brook Road, Bootle,
January 5th, 1910.

Dear Mr. BULLEY,
    The above Committee learn with gratification that you are taking up the **Workers' battle in Rossendale**. We wish you every **success** and hope that **EVERY Trade Unionist** in the Constituency will give you their hearty support, knowing, as we do, how valuable an acquisition you would be to the cause we are working for, if **returned to Parliament.**

Yours faithfully, ARTHUR W. SHORT.

Mr. A. K. BULLEY.

WORKERS! FOLLOW THIS ADVICE

By voting for BULLEY

Printed and Published by C. Hargreaves, Burnley Road, Waterloo.

MUNICIPAL ELECTION, WEDNESDAY, NOV. 1st, 1911,
From 8 a.m. to 8 p.m.

KENSINGTON WARD

A. K. BULLEY,
LABOUR CANDIDATE.

saw him coming, he shouted 'Mr Bulley!' down the hatch, and the staff knew what to produce!

To some people he was almost impossible to understand, even if a common love of alpine plants kept them together. This was so for Reginald Farrer, who lived as a member of the gentry on the family estate at Ingleborough, Yorkshire. Once, when Bulley was visiting Farrer, their evening stroll round the garden was interrupted by the dressing bell. This meant nothing to Bulley, who, in due course, turned up for dinner wearing the same clothes as when he arrived. He departed in the morning, and a few days later a parcel arrived from Farrer's address. Excitement mounted as Bulley opened the parcel expecting some plants, but it contained clothes which the butler had unpacked and put in a drawer. No wonder that Farrer wrote to another plant collector, 'I rather wish, in the course of your peregrinations, you would come in contact with him [Bulley], and see what you think. He's a queer bird, but I do really like him.'[18]

But Bulley was bothered about more important things than conventions of dress and social etiquette. He was clear in his mind that the government should reduce the intense overcrowding in the city. After a glorious May with blossoms abounding in his garden, he wrote, 'It's a shame that so few people have gardens to enjoy. I believe that bye and bye the State won't allow these hideous, gardenless streets, which take all the joy out of life.'[19] Meanwhile he would crusade for change.

Twice he wrote in his notebook:

> I will not cease from mental fight,
> Nor shall my sword sleep in my hand,
> Till we have built Jerusalem
> In England's green and pleasant land. (BLAKE)

When addressing socialist meetings in a very poor area of Liverpool, Bulley was known to ask, with passion, 'Your land: I wonder how many of you own a plant pot full of it?'

Through the Labour movement he heard of Margaret McMillan, a leading socialist who saw gardens as places of healing and nurture for children in the slums. She constructed a garden in the urban waste of Deptford, London, so that children could camp in the garden and 'pale faces brightened at the sight of the sweet williams and white fox-gloves' which they could see from their bed.[20] The idea appealed to Bulley, who showed lantern slides about it in his electioneering.

When he bought land for a garden, he shared it. He immediately opened it for all the public to enjoy – free – every day of the year except Christmas Day. He began his nursery as a co-operative, with the trade mark 'All to gather, all together' and started penny packets of seed so that flowers could be grown in even a flowerpot or a window box. He provided a field for football, and space for bowling greens and tennis courts.

A special feature of his garden was the large number of new and rare plants which Bulley was introducing to this country. It made a unique collection, and when Bulley reached his sixties, he was elected by the Council of the Royal Horticultural Society to receive the highest honour that the Society could give: the Victoria Medal of Honour. It had been instituted in 1897, in celebration of the Queen's Diamond Jubilee. This gold medal can only be held by 60 people at any one time, and recipients have included such outstanding people as Sir Joseph Hooker, Gertrude Jekyll and George Forrest. But Bulley did not want a 'riband to stick in his coat'. His socialist principles remained paramount. He eschewed acceptance of the honour. The Council received a letter from him, 'declining the V.M.H. on the ground that he had a strong objection to decorations of any kind.'[21]

The trademark of 'The Co-operative Bees, Ltd' in 1905.

After Bulley died, a relative wrote to his son Alfred: 'Your father was a most unusual man, with an intelligence beyond most. What he believed, that he would follow at all costs, but his convictions had to be absolute.'[22] In this way he was his father's son, following his own ideas and convictions with tenacity and determination. Born into an adventurous, stimulating and spirited family at the height of the British Empire, he used his energy and enterprise to introduce new and rare plants from many far-flung places. He combined his passion with Bulley business acumen and a sense of sharing which was greatly to benefit both science and horticulture. It was a timely and fruitful combination of talent, personality and circumstance.

2

West Kirby: Springboard to Success

Cultivate a hobby … It gives a fine pleasure to life (BULLEY, 1926).[1]

Never could Bulley have foreseen, in his early thirties, what train of events would emerge from his passion for plants. But, at first unwittingly, and then more purposefully, he was laying foundations for his future role in the introduction of new plants into Britain. It all began in a small way in West Kirby, Cheshire, where he spent eight formative years. His botanical knowledge and gardening skills were honed, he started to obtain seeds from across the globe and he received some wise advice which guided his future.

A flourishing field club

In their early years in West Kirby, Arthur Bulley and his wife enjoyed happy outings with the Liverpool Naturalists' Field Club. It was one of the earliest natural history clubs, founded in 1860, to 'call forth latent taste in Natural History', and ladies could join in. This was a novelty for 'The opportunity it affords of pursuing a pleasing study in company with that sex whose presence doubles the enjoyment both of rural rambles and of scientific investigation.' It was a respectable hobby in the healthy fresh air, inspired by popular books such as Philip Gosse's *The Romance of Natural History* and Frank Buckland's *Curiosities of Natural History*. When the club was founded, there was a nationwide craze for collecting flowers and ferns, shells and birds' eggs, seaweeds and butterflies, and nearly 400 people joined the Liverpool club in its first few months! In 1866, 350 members went on an excursion to the Great Orme.[2]

Liverpool Naturalists' Field Club
ESTABLISHED 1860
FOR THE PRACTICAL STUDY OF NATURAL HISTORY.
ON FRIDAY, SOIREE 29TH JANY 1892.
at the Royal Institution, Colquitt Street.
COMPLIMENTARY TICKET.
(NOT TRANSFERABLE.)
DOORS OPEN AT 6-
Carriages may be ordered for 10 o'Clock.
JAMES MACKARELL,
HON. SEC.

Mr and Mrs A K Bulley both joined the Liverpool Naturalists' Field Club in the early 1890s.

When the Bulleys joined in 1890, the membership had fallen to less than 300, with sometimes fewer than 50 at a meeting, but it was buoyant, with very knowledgeable leaders. The Revd H H Higgins was still the revered president, after 28 devoted years. He spent all his spare time in the study of natural history and proudly boasted that the Liverpool Naturalists' Field Club was a household word from John O'Groats to the Channel Islands. The botanical referee, who checked all plant identifications, was Robert Brown, an unrivalled local botanist who collected 1200 species of flowering plants in Lancashire and Cheshire.

Bulley immediately made his mark, and the annual reports give us the earliest information on his prowess as a botanist. During a discussion at his first evening meeting on 13 November 1890, 'Mr. A. K. Bulley mentioned several new localities where he had found some of the rarest plants of our district.'[3] The next month, Robert Brown reported, 'Our member, Mr. A. Bulley, made some interesting finds near Burton Rock.' The following year, Bulley went on at least six excursions, which ranged from Malham Cove to Llangollen and Formby. During these excursions, prizes were awarded for naming or collecting the greatest number of species, and there was a special prize, called the 'Botanical Enigma', which was awarded for solving a puzzle of plant identification, and finding that plant. In 1891 Bulley won seven prizes! He was obviously enjoying himself hugely.

On a pleasant Saturday summer afternoon in 1891, there was a field meeting at Helsby, near Chester. (A boy was paid 1s 6d for carrying a plank for use in crossing the ditches on the marsh.) The party of 44 people searched for all the plants they could find from the marsh to Helsby Hill, tea was provided in a large room in the village, and the prizes were awarded. First prize, naming the greatest number of plants in flower and fruit, went to Miss E M Wood, with 116 species. But 'This occasioned the keenest competition on record, Mr A. K. Bulley taking the second place, with 114 species.' The Botanical Enigma was solved, and the plant, *Prunella vulgaris*, was found by nine others and Mr A K Bulley.[4] What a satisfying afternoon, and what a pleasant change from cotton brokering.

Bulley excelled at the Botanical Enigma Prize. It was not meant for the merely casual observer happy to know the English names of a few flowers. It required botanical expertise and great attention to detail, and was a competition designed by Revd H H Higgins to teach the identification and Latin names of plants. The technical facts of a particular plant were given on an envelope, and that flower had to be found and identified during the excursion. For example, in July 1891, the following details were given on a field meeting at Malham Cove and Gordale Scar, in Yorkshire:

> Leaves opposite, the radical ones very variable, those on the stem deeply pinnatified. Flowers capitate. Involucel eight furrowed. Corolla monopetalous, tubular, five cleft. Stamens four.
> Answer: *Scabiosa columbaria* (small scabious)

Through the field club, Bulley was not only enjoying his hobby but keeping up to date with the Latin names of plants. It was important to him to be on top of his subject. He owned the 12 volumes of Sowerby's *English Botany* (third edition, published in 1885) and he had ready access to the *Index Kewensis*, but botanists' knowledge of the British flora was still incomplete, and amateur experts such as Robert Brown were invaluable for finding the latest information. When reporting on the Malham excursion, Robert Brown wrote: 'One of the good finds made was the *Hieracium gibsoni* of Backhouse, this plant is only found in this part of Yorkshire, this being the only station in the British Isles. The find … has been identified as the true *gibsoni* by Mr Hanbury, who is writing a monograph on this difficult genus.'[5]

This trip to Malham, with its geological and botanical interest and fine scenery, was the excursion of the season for everyone. 'Upwards of 70 members and friends met at the Exchange Station, and proceeded by special train at 9.38 a.m. to Hellifield, where waggonettes [horse-drawn, four-wheeled, open vehicles] were in waiting to convey the party to Malham, a

---

Liverpool Naturalists' Field Club, 1892.

President.
REV. H. H. HIGGINS, M.A.

Vice-Presidents.
J. SHAW, and G. H. MORTON, F.G.S.

Committee.

THOS. BIRKS,
ROBERT BROWN,
A. K. BULLEY,
Miss M. E. CLEMENTSON,
EDWARD DAVIES, F.C.S., &c.,
J. J. FITZPATRICK,

H. S. GIBSON,
J. SIBLEY HICKS, F.R.C.S., &c.
W. H. HOLT,
JOSIAH MARPLES,
P. McDONALD, B.A.
Miss E. M. WOOD.

Botanical Referee.
ROBERT BROWN.

Hon. Treasurer.
W. H. WILKINSON.

Hon. Secretary.
JAS. MACKARELL.

FOURTH FIELD MEETING AT

MOEL FAMMAU,

On THURSDAY, JUNE 23rd.

LEAVE Liverpool Landing Stage at 9.0, and Woodside Station at 9.25, arriving at Mold, 10.53. Waggonettes will be in waiting to convey the party to the nearest point for the ascent of Moel Fammau (about 6 miles); the distance to the summit being 1½ miles. The view from the ridge and from the summit in clear weather is one of the finest in Wales. Abundance of time for natural history work will be afforded— the waggonettes returning at 3.30 p.m.

Those who desire a quieter walk may leave the vehicles at "The Loggerheads," three miles from Mold, and spend the time up to 4 o'clock in exploring the beautiful valley of the Alyn, which is rich in botanical rarities.

DINNER-TEA will be served at the Black Lion Hotel, Mold, (Mr. Maddox, proprietor) at 5.30, after which the prizes will be awarded.

RETURN from Mold at 7.41, due in Liverpool, 9.15.

Order Prize for *Linaceæ*, *Ericaceæ*, and *Scrophulariaceæ*.
Basket of Wild Flowers.

TICKETS, (Exclusive of waggonettes, for which 2/. each will be charged)—Members, 5/6, Non-Members, 6/6, may be obtained at Messrs. KER & SONS, 11, Basnett Street, **up to 6 o'clock p.m. on TUESDAY, 21st**, after which 1/- each additional will be charged.

N.B.—Holders of late tickets cannot be guaranteed seats in conveyances.

Members are reminded that if unable to use their tickets they can have the amount of railway fare returned on application to the Treasurer within two days.

JAS. MACKARELL,
Hon. Secretary.
PRESELAND ROAD, GREAT CROSBY.

A K Bulley was a committee member of the Liverpool Naturalists' Field Club and competed keenly for prizes at field meetings.

pleasant drive of 8 miles.' They had a walk, followed by an excellent tea-dinner at the Breck Hotel, where the prizes were awarded. Then the evening drive back by waggonettes to Hellifield was 'much enjoyed, though some of the ladies were alarmed at the downhill pace.' They reached Liverpool at 10 p.m.

So increased knowledge and pleasure were happily intertwined, and the expertise of members was used to update *The Flora of Liverpool*. Appendices were added as more was learned of the flora growing within 15 miles of the town hall, and in 1893 Bulley was brought on to the committee appointed to write a completely new flora. It was a painstaking task as each committee member had to write out a few pages of the old flora at home, and these were amended at the next session of the committee. Funding was a problem, but when the revised flora was published in 1902, A K Bulley was one of those 'whose donations helped forward the work.'[6] His initials AKB were printed in the flora beside the plants he discovered at new locations such as Hilbre Island, West Kirby and Burton Rock.

This experience with a local flora later helped Bulley to understand the need for a scientific study of the vegetation of other areas of the world. He appreciated the value of herbarium specimens for plant identification. So when he became a patron of plant hunters, he accepted that they should spend time gathering specimens for drying and sending to the herbariums of botanical gardens. So his patronage was doubly beneficial, to science as well as horticulture. In contrast, it seems that his future rival, Harry J Veitch, was unwilling for Ernest Wilson to 'waste' time collecting lots of plant specimens when he first began collecting in China.

Meanwhile, Bulley's interest in the field club began to wane. At first he turned up regularly for field excursions, whatever the weather and mud. At evening meetings he took part in lively discussions. But maybe it was insufficiently demanding, or too parochial, and the President, Revd H H Higgins, died in 1893. There were also competing claims on his time. In 1892 he was elected to the Liverpool Literary and Philosophical Society, and in 1896 he joined the Liverpool Geographical Society. Bulley's gardening interests increased and his horizons were expanding. The Bulleys resigned from the field club in 1897, before they moved from West Kirby.

However, the love of local wild plants never left him. Cycling was becoming popular, pneumatic tyres were available, and cyclists could go faster than cars, which were limited to 4 mph. The Bulleys cycled all over the Wirral with a botanical notebook cut at the corners so that it could fit into Bulley's pocket, and making happy jokes about the English names of plants like 'yellow archangel' and 'weasel's snout'. Moreover, Bulley was keen that everyone should always have access to the countryside, so he was an enthusiastic member of the Wirral Footpaths and Open Spaces Preservation Society and the National Trust. In future years he was to give generously towards purchasing land for public access. In 1917 he and two other men bought 64 acres (26 ha) of land on Thurstaston Hill so that people could enjoy this beauty spot and in 1928 he and Mrs Bulley presented 20.5 acres (8.3 ha) of Burton Wood to the National Trust.

But what else would absorb Bulley's boundless energies? His mind focused increasingly on the fascination of alpine flowers. On holidays in the Alps and Pyrenees, 'admiring Nature in her wildest grace', he observed the exquisite beauty of small alpine flowers and he gradually built up a collection of them in his garden on Darmonds Green, West Kirby. He was gripped by the joy of discovering and growing them. His botanical knowledge and his love of wild and garden flowers were joining together in one joyous new purpose – to experiment with new flowers to grow in the garden. There began a never-ending and insatiable appetite for acquiring 'new and rare out-of-the-way' alpine and hardy flowers to try out in his garden. His aim was no less than the discovery of new plants which would thrive and beautify our gardens.

A global quest

With the mind of a frontiersman, eager for discovery, Bulley's search for new plants became a personal obsession. It was a quest fired by altruism and driven by the competitive urge of a dynamic individual. He had an insatiable curiosity like the Elephant's Child in Kipling's *Just So Stories* (a favourite book in the family). His brain was hyperactive as he combed the catalogues, read the gardening papers and wrote to any possible candidate who might send him seeds. It was the acquisitive energetic curiosity of a keen Victorian collector, confident that the worldwide span of plant variety in temperate and alpine areas could be harnessed to bring beauty to our gardens.

Exploration was opening up new areas of the globe, and new concepts had been developed on the geography of plants. The brilliant Prussian scientist and explorer, Alexander von Humboldt (1769–1859), had dramatically demonstrated the relationship between climate and vegetation in one of the highest volcanic ranges in the world, the Andes, in 1802. By systematically recording botanical and meteorological data, he was able to show altitudinal changes from the tropical lowlands to the snow-covered peaks. From his writings it became recognised that 'temperate' and 'alpine' plants could be found at high altitudes in the tropics as well as at lower altitudes towards the polar regions. This opened up enormous possibilities for finding new plants.

Bulley wanted to exploit this potential. He was influenced by William Robinson who had written *Alpine Flowers for English Gardens* in 1870 to dispel the notion that alpine flowers could not be grown in gardens. Some very distinguished gardeners held this conservative view, including the Duke of Argyll, who regretted that although gardeners 'had overcome almost every difficulty of cultivation, they were conquered by one – that of growing alpine plants.' How amazed this duke would be to see the present popularity of alpine plants, and the many shows of the thriving Alpine Garden Society! But it has been a long road to success, and Bulley was one of the pioneers who, at the close of the nineteenth century, answered Robinson's call to try out new plants and broaden people's vision.

Orchidomania had filled the heated Victorian conservatories with lush exotic blooms, a fern craze followed and carpet bedding prevailed in parks and many gardens as Bulley worked with his little alpine gems in his West Kirby garden. In Liverpool the greenhouses of gentlemen still overflowed with tropical luxuriousness and in London only a small audience heard a talk on alpines at the Royal Horticultural Society (RHS) in 1891. At Kew the alpine house and rockery were both enlarged in the 1890s but it was the autumn of 1903 before the RHS started a special class for 'Alpines and Rock Gardens' at their grand Summer Temple Show in London (before there was a Chelsea Flower Show). The RHS was almost a hundred years old before it thus welcomed this new movement in gardening.

Bulley was determined, but his personal path to his goal was not straightforward. He yearned to travel himself to collect seed, but there had been a long-term decline in the price of cotton and in 1897–8 prices slumped to an all-time low point just as Bulley was buying land for a bigger garden. He could not travel, either. He had to rest his hopes in the future, saying, 'Given prosperity I'll go myself some day.'[7] He was to wait many moons, because of the realities of the daily demands of his job. In retirement he went round the world, but not 'roughing it' like a seasoned collector. And it is not certain that he would ever have been willing to put up with the hard conditions of far-off places for long enough. He was too used to places such as the Grand Hotel, London! The Bulleys enjoyed alpine huts on holidays in the Alps, but months of rat-ridden inns in the Andes were probably not really appealing.

Even the next best thing, having his own collector, eluded him for years (except for occasional short forays within Europe). There seems to have been an anti-commercial principle at stake. 'There are few things in the wide world I should enjoy more than sending out a collector. But at present [about 1897] it's impossible. I won't sell plants, and I can't afford the expense without selling.'[8] As a keen socialist and sharer, giving away and exchanging plants, there was probably an inherent conflict within him: to share, as a hobby, or enter commerce. The non-selling principle held for several years until he tired of the frustrations and difficulties!

Throughout the 1890s, Bulley dreamed his dreams and carried on his search as best he could. Inevitably success was patchy. There is no record of seed from Australia, and few contacts in mountainous areas of South America. But after intense networking and postal activity he amassed a seed collection of amazing scope. Seed came from as far as the Falkland Islands in the southern hemisphere and from the USA, China, Japan and Siberia in the northern hemisphere. His collection also contained some stunning flowers such as the beautiful blue 'Chilean crocus', *Tecophilea cyanocrocus*. This grew wild only in Chile and may have been more abundant then; now collecting and grazing have probably made it almost extinct. Another 'winner' for which he hunted for years was the only yellow autumn crocus, *Crocus scharojanii*, from the Caucasus region. This was one of the flowers which Bulley obtained before Kew did so.

He approached his collecting task in a number of different ways. First he sought inspiration and seeds from fellow enthusiasts and nurserymen in the vanguard of the alpine gardening movement. One was Max Leichtlin of Baden Baden, a plant collector who obtained new plants and bulbs from the 'ends of the earth', tried them out and propagated them to send and swap with people such as Bulley. Another was Henri Correvon (1854–1939) in Switzerland. Correvon was a leading light on alpine plants, a nurseryman and a regular columnist in the English gardening press. He became a good friend and lasting influence on Bulley, and later signed his name in one of Bulley's gardening books. Other nurserymen he visited were Smith of the Daisy Hill Nursery, Newry, Thompson of Ipswich and Backhouse of York, whilst he wrote to others from Yokohama, Japan to Christchurch, New Zealand and Boulder, Colorado, USA.

Secondly, Bulley sought seeds from botanic gardens. On the continent he contacted botanic gardens as far as St Petersburg on the Baltic and Tiflis in Georgia, hoping to gain seeds of wild plants growing in their different hinterlands as well as those obtained through their own networks. He was like the famous alpine gardener, Farrer, who said 'I cannot steal, though to beg I am by no means ashamed.'

Thirdly, his correspondence in the 1890s produced seed from a wide range of people. These included a paid plant collector in New Zealand, a missionary botanist in Hakadate, Japan, a customs officer in China, and a consul working on a Burma–Yunnan Boundary Commission. Conan Doyle would have been proud of Bulley's detective work!

Kew was an obvious Mecca, as the botanical centre of the Empire. Its bulletin was packed with pertinent information on 'new and noteworthy plants'. Its seeds could not be bought. To obtain seeds Bulley had to be a regular correspondent, subscribe to the bulletin, or produce a list of seeds for exchange. Bulley did all of these things.

He began to send plants to Kew in 1895 and irregular letters went to and fro for 38 years, his first letters being addressed to the director, Professor (later Sir) W T Thiselton-Dyer, whilst his offers of plants and seeds were recorded in the 'Inwards Book' at Kew. Bulley's offers of seed packets made a startling jump in a surprisingly quick time, from none in 1895 to nearly 500 packets in the first half of 1898. But he became 'pretty sick of this job. It has practically taken up all my evenings for the last 2 months. I get home and grind steadily till bed time. It's no joke and costs a good deal of money. Of course it's very nice to think one has aided in adding to the available beauty of the world. But I repeat it's no joke.'[9]

Bulley was definitely feeling underappreciated and at odds with the director at Kew when he wrote this letter to him. He had tried to build up a rapport

Sir William T Thiselton-Dyer (1843–1928), Director of Kew 1885–1905.

with Thiselton-Dyer but to little avail. He had begun by sending seeds eagerly and willingly, feeling honoured to be adding to the 'National Collection' and writing, 'To add to the store of beauty in the world by giving beautiful things to those who will care for them, is to me an unmixed pleasure.'[10] But when there were misunderstandings and seed packets were not acknowledged, and questions were left unanswered, his sense of public duty was strained. He sent Kew 'Lord only knows how many packets of seed', some of them new to Kew, but he seemed to gain nothing in return. The disappointment was grievous. In the spring of 1898 he wrote to Dyer, 'Will you allow me to say, with the utmost good will, that the [seed] list always seems to me quite below what we ought to get from Kew's unrivalled opportunities.' He was speaking of the 'Hardy Herbaceous and Alpine things' and rubbed in his point by saying 'I seldom see anything good which cannot be got from nurserymen; and this is certainly not true of St Petersburg.'[11]

Dyer's defence is not recorded. However, the following spring Bulley was busy striking cuttings and sending seed of new plants he had received from the Peloponnesian Alps and Chile … and he did obtain from Kew a trained gardener, Sharp, with whom he was well pleased!

Sir David Prain (1857–1944), Director of Kew (1905–1922).

Bulley also wrote to Kew's largest outstation, The Royal Botanical Gardens, Calcutta. This was considered the greatest botanical establishment of the British Empire. It had the largest and best-trained staff and access to the Himalayas. This was a vital step in Bulley's quest.

The potential of the Himalayas had already been demonstrated by Joseph Dalton Hooker when he explored the mountains of Sikkim in the middle of the nineteenth century. He discovered many beautiful rhododendrons, and although Bulley was never to be a total devotee of these plants, he did hanker after an exceptionally fine one introduced by Hooker. He wrote to the Royal Botanic Garden, Edinburgh: 'Amongst your Himalayan Rhododendrons have you R. campylocarpum? If so, can you get some seed from it this year? I'm awfully "gone" on it, and as it comes from over 11,000' [3350 m] alt. in Sikkim, I don't see why it shouldn't be hardy.'[12] Later he was able to report triumphantly, 'Your seedling … has gone through the winter without turning a hair,' and satisfaction reigned.[13]

For Bulley the Himalayan primulas were even more exciting. Primula sikkimensis and P. capitata were both found by Hooker in Sikkim. 'What a glorious colour P. capitata is,' Bulley sighed happily as he gazed at its purplish, tight, disc-like head of flowers. He found no trouble in growing it, but, like others, he had much greater difficulty with the then recently discovered Primula reidii. He obtained it time and time again, he loved the colour and scent of this flower so much. Indeed he pronounced himself to be 'madly in love' with primulas,[14] which was an excellent stimulus for finding more!

Plate 1. Meconopsis integrifolia. *Grown from Russian seed at the nursery of A. Bee & Co., Neston. There was such excitement that Mr Bulley called in Mary Wroe to draw it, and sent the illustration to William Robinson who published it in Flora & Sylva vol III no.24 March 1905.*

MECONOPSIS INTEGRIFOLIA

(Left) **Plate 2.** Rhododendron forrestii, *discovered by Forrest in Yunnan just before he was nearly killed by Lamas in 1905.*

(Below) **Plate 3.** Rhododendron impeditum, *discovered by Forrest, who collected seed in 1910 on his second expedition for Bees Ltd.*

Plates 4 and 5.
Pieris formosa
forrestii at Ness
Botanic Gardens. Here it
was grown from Forrest's
first packet of Yunnan
seed sent to Bees Ltd.

(*Above left*) **Plate 6.**
The Ness pine wood,
planted by Bulley
c.1912.

(*Above right*) **Plate 7.**
Primula bulleyana,
self-sown by Bulley's
pond in the rock garden
at Ness.

(Left) **Plate 8.**
Geranium farreri
in the rockery at Ness.

The botanic gardens in Calcutta were established for commercial purposes, but this did not stop Bulley asking the curator, Dr David Prain, for seed of new and rare ornamental plants from the Himalayas. The staff trained the Lepcha people of Sikkim to collect plants and seed for them, and Prain sent Bulley seed until he left Calcutta to become Director of Kew in 1905. His access to Sikkim made a lasting impression on Bulley, and he recalled it later in his life when he sent one of his own collectors there. Meanwhile he continued contact with Prain at Kew until Prain retired in 1922. He was one of the experts whose lives threaded in and out of Bulley's own life in a great skein of contacts which Bulley maintained for the next 20–30 years.

However, Bulley's strong independent streak made him want to obtain seed from areas untouched by nurserymen or the colonial network. It was missionaries who often reached the furthest, far-off places and in March 1896 Bulley reported, 'I hope shortly to have some interesting seeds in as I have been writing to missionaries in all sorts of out of the way places in the temperate regions of the globe, asking them to send seeds. Doubtless I shall get much rubbish, but there may be some good things.'[15]

At least his optimism was tempered by realism, for this method was like a giant lottery with very little chance of success. It depended on where the missionaries lived, whether they knew one plant from another, whether they could appreciate the importance of collecting ripe seed, whether they dried it properly so that it arrived in good condition. They might describe only the colour of the flower or the height or hairiness of the plant, with no accompanying dried plant material or habitat notes. So propagation could only be based on guess work, trial and error, and after all that trouble, he might discover that some plants were not hardy enough to grow out of doors, while others were no prettier than weeds. Looking back at this time, Bulley did not have entirely happy memories: 'In ancient days I stuck on one, a French missionary at Nagasaki. He sent me a wad of seeds — composites and umbellifers to a man!'[16] It was a family joke that his garden was in danger of possessing the best international collection of dandelions.

However, Bulley could never resist an opportunity if there was the slightest hope of success. What about missionaries in China? After all, in the *Kew Bulletin* of the 1890s, French Jesuit missionaries in China were drawing attention to

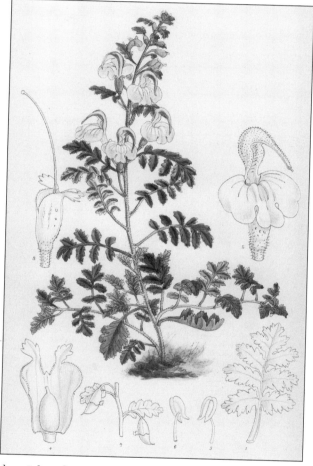

Pedicularis curvipes, native of Sikkim Himalaya. Introduced by Bulley with seed from the Royal Botanic Gardens, Calcutta. In 1900, his plant was illustrated in Curtis's Botanical Magazine (t7735), and described by Sir Joseph Hooker.

the rich flora in the mountains. The *Gardeners' Chronicle* pointed out that the opening up of the Celestial Empire meant that both new species and the originals of many garden plants could now be found.

There was a huge increase in the number of missionaries in China in the 1890s, more than 2800 of them, and over half of them British. They seemed to be Bulley's greatest hope for cheaply gathering seed from the unexplored mountains. In 1897, of the 240 British subjects resident there, 232 were Protestant missionaries and their families. So Bulley tried his luck. 'I've written to the C.I.M. [China Inland Mission] people there [Tali, Yunnan] offering all sorts of bribes. Shortly I shall tackle the papists.'[17] There was immense rivalry between missionaries, but Bulley took no sides. He approached any in order to maximise his chances of getting seed. Although he was an agnostic, if any missionary box was thrust in front of him he would give a donation in case one of their missionaries might be useful. Later he reported: 'I'm getting a full list of the Papist Missionaries from Rome. Shades of my Puritan Ancestors!' One of these was Père Soulié (1858–1905) who travelled widely in the mountains on the Tibetan-Chinese border and sent over 7000 dried specimens to Paris before he was murdered by Tibetan monks.

In Bulley's List of Seeds for Exchange, circulated from West Kirby in 1897–8,[18] seeds from Ningpo, Shansi, Yunnan and the Tibet frontier are all likely to have been from missionaries (see map). It is impossible to gauge the overall level of success with propagating these seeds, but below is one example of a missionary's name being given to a plant which Bulley grew from his seed.

The plant was *Ceratostigma polhilli* (now *C. minus* Stapf.), and the missionary was Mr Cecil Polhill-Turner. He was a member of the China Inland Mission at

Seeds offered for exchange from different parts of the world by A K Bulley, c.1898. Source: List of Seeds for Exchange, A K Bulley, West Kirby, Cheshire. Held at the Royal Botanic Garden, Edinburgh.

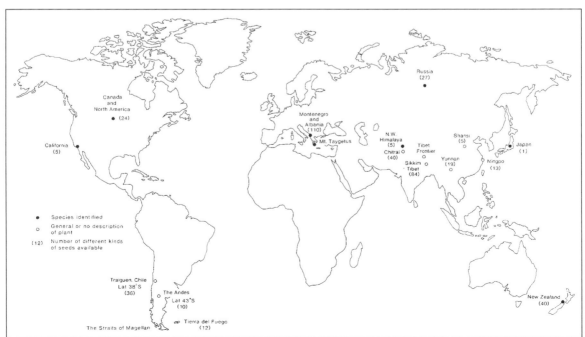

Tachien-lu (now named Kangding) in Szechuan for three years, from 1897 to 1900. It is a story which reflects those high Victorian days of missionary verve when there was abounding vitality in the Protestant churches in Britain. Many missionaries were from an artisan or tradesman's background, but in 1885 Britain was startled at the news that seven young men of high social standing were giving up everything, their cricket and rowing, their polo, hunting and

shooting, to give their lives 'for higher things and nobler purposes'. They became known as 'The Cambridge Seven', because they were all students at Cambridge University. Two of them were brothers, Cecil and Arthur Polhill-Turner. They were both old Etonians, Cecil an officer in the Queen's Bays and Arthur a theological student.[19]

They sailed for China in 1885, with only a slender knowledge of the language. Wearing Chinese dress and pigtails, the two brothers took a river steamer up the Yangtze river to the distant province of Szechuan. Arthur stayed for ten years in a remote area

with no proper roads, just mountain paths and narrow stone-paved tracks, while Cecil travelled more widely. Both of them may have been commissioned to send Bulley seeds, for in April 1899 Bulley reported that he had received two batches of seeds from missionaries in the alps of western Szechuan but we are only certain of Cecil, because it was he who went to Tachien-lu, whence the seeds of the future *Ceratostigma polhilli* were sent to Bulley. This town lies at 2700 m in the Chinese-Tibetan frontier land, on one of the main routes to Tibet, with views up ravines to range upon range of snow-capped mountains. It had already been visited by a few other naturalists, but there was ample scope for collecting, and it is interesting to note that Bulley obtained some seed from there before the plant collector Ernest Wilson ever arrived.

In 1900 both these missionary brothers' stay came to an abrupt end. They and their families were forced to flee for safety to the coast after the Emperor Dowager sent a telegram to the Viceroy of Szechuan to 'Kill all Foreigners in your Province'. As the number of missionaires had increased, so did Chinese suspicion and fear of them. Hatred was gradually organised into the Boxer Rising which aimed to stone, torment, imprison, persecute or kill Christians. Antipathy to foreigners welled up in the summer of 1900 and a Boxer song declared that 'foreigners were devils not men'. Boxers hissed *iang-kuei-tsi* at them, meaning 'foreign devil'. Banners proclaimed 'By Imperial command exterminate the Christian Religion'. During 1900, 136 Protestant missionaries and 53 children were martyred in China. So it is no wonder that a postcard from Bulley, written in July 1900 and taped in the 'Inwards Book' at Kew, comments, 'A lot of fresh seeds just in from Szechuan. I hope the good fellow who sent them is still alive.'[20]

'The Cambridge Seven', c. 1885: students from Cambridge University who became missionaries in China. At least one, Cecil Polhill-Turner, sent seeds to A K Bulley and is seated second from right.

Bulley shared the seed with both the botanic gardens of Kew and Edinburgh and Bulley asked that Mr Polhill-Turner's name should be associated with it. *Ceratostigma polhilli* was described as a new species. It grew to a bush over a metre high against a wall in the Edinburgh Botanic Garden but its small pale blue flowers died in the frost. It is a tender plant in Britain. However, Bulley grew it at Ness, and in 1905, when eventually he had his own nursery, its catalogue proudly stated *Ceratostigma polhilli*, 'offered for sale for the first time' at the, then, expensive price of 7s 6d.

Meanwhile, Bulley received some strong advice on how productive the mountains of south-west China could be. In March 1897 Henri Correvon wrote him a postcard in idiosyncratic English:

> If you know somebody which is in the Yunnan you must write … All the plants of Delavay came from there. Read the publication of Franchet on the new Primula; … Gentians, Paeonias, Anemones, Iriss [irises], etc. of the Yunnan. I always wish to hear that somebody would go there … if you have a friend there ask him for seeds … faithfully yours H Correvon.[21]

Fortunately for Bulley, he had already found one! He was Dr Augustine Henry (1857–1930), a scholarly Irishman in the Chinese customs service. He was stationed in Mengsi, Yunnan, when Bulley first wrote to him in November 1896 and he had already collected bulbs of the beautiful orange-flowered lily, *Lilium henryi*, which is still widely grown in gardens today. Plant collecting was his hobby and he had been collecting in China for 12 years, sending his plant specimens to Kew. He received very enthusiastic letters from Bulley and he began to send him seeds and epiphytic orchids early in 1897.

The first parcel was a cigar-box containing 85 kinds of seeds from the area around Mengsi. For Bulley this was a breakthrough, because the seeds were listed and numbered, with remarks on each number. Henry warned that they might not all be hardy, but Bulley was still excited and very grateful. It is not surprising that Henry reported to a friend, 'Mr. Bulley seemed satisfied with the seeds I sent him and wrote me a letter full of flattery and appreciation.'[22] They took to each other, and Henry wrote that Bulley was 'an enthusiast. I have a weakness for enthusiasts, cranks and the like.' He was a kind, good-natured person and seemed fascinated by Bulley's ideas – 'a bit of a Fabian, who wants to introduce beautiful plants to the cottages of the poor.'[23] He sent Bulley further seeds, and one happy outcome was the flowering of *Begonia cathayana* by Bulley and the publication of his introduction in the prestigious *Curtis's Botanical Magazine* (plate 8202).

Bulley was so keen to meet Henry that he booked him for a visit three-and-a-half years ahead, when Henry was due to be in England in 1901. He confessed, 'I badly want to have a yarn with you about all sorts of things.' There is no doubt that these talks helped to persuade Bulley that the best way forward was for him to hire his own plant collector. Henry was an invaluable spur.

Meanwhile, it was a botanist in India who guided Bulley in another way. This was John Duthie, superintendent of the Botanic Garden, Saharanpur, in the north-west province and discoverer of *Primula reidii*. He recommended

Bulley to contact Professor Isaac Bayley Balfour at the Royal Botanic Garden, Edinburgh, and he can hardly ever have given better advice to anyone. In contrast to Bulley's early disappointments with Kew, Balfour was encouraging, understanding and brought the best out of Bulley. Moreover, when Bulley finally decided to hire a professional plant hunter in Yunnan, China, Balfour provided the ideal man and continued as Bulley's mentor.

Bulley and Balfour

19 October 1896

Dear Mr Bulley

I carried away from Liverpool a very pleasing recollection of your wonderful gardening skill. How you manage to grow so many fine things … has astonished me.[24]

This was high praise from the Regius Keeper of the Royal Botanic Garden, Edinburgh, Professor Isaac Bayley Balfour, whose other official title was 'Queen's Botanist in Scotland'.

Balfour had just seen Bulley's West Kirby garden, tucked into the sunny side of a sandstone ridge and packed with unusual and rare flowers. They were mainly hardy herbaceous and alpine plants, grown out of doors and tended with the greatest loving care, pandered to their every whim like little personalities, and adored by Bulley for their exquisite charm, rarity and beauty.

Balfour was a man of wide experience, he was in his third professorship, after being Professor of Botany in the universities of Glasgow and Oxford. He had been to Rodriguez to observe the transit of Venus and botanised on the Island of Socotra. Why should this eminent and busy man, head of a great national garden, bother to visit this plant enthusiast on the margin of a small town on the commuting line to Liverpool? The answer lies partly in the

Sir Isaac Bayley Balfour (1853–1922), Regius Keeper and Queen's, later King's, Botanist, Royal Botanic Garden, Edinburgh, 1888–1922.

greatness of the man and his willingness to help others. A genuine interest in plants was a passport to his friendship and he had a warm corner in his heart for keen horticultural amateurs. He recognised their important role in horticultural progress and felt it his duty to encourage them. He must also have been intrigued by Bulley's ability to obtain rare plant seed from across the globe, his tenacity in the hunt, complemented by his willingness to experiment, his patient perseverance in the garden. In short, Bulley himself was a rare find and Balfour was curious to meet him.

Moreover, Bulley's rock garden was of particular interest to Balfour. Although the rock garden in Edinburgh was well established and famous, Balfour confessed that his collection of plants was at 'low water', and he was eager to see for himself what Bulley grew in his garden.

Balfour was rather bowed down by heavy administrative and teaching responsibilities, and Bulley's letters were a welcome refreshment, full of vigour and individuality. The two men had corresponded for only seven months when Balfour came to West Kirby, but already their inborn love of flowers was drawing them together, and they had a matching enthusiasm and fascination for introducing new flowers to Britain. Their correspondence was to continue for over 25 years, until Balfour died in 1922. It was a friendship which was to benefit them both, and to contribute greatly to a golden era of plant exploration.

It all began by Bulley requesting a seed list. It was March 1896, and Bulley wrote, in his characteristic spiky writing, to the curator of the Royal Botanic Garden at Edinburgh. His letter must have caught Balfour's eye because, in exchange, Bulley offered any seed from a fascinating list of 26 'of the more out of the way seeds collected in my garden.'[25] These included now classic rock garden plants which were rare then, such as *Ramonda myconi* and *Iris reticulata* 'Krelagei'. Some of them were not grown in Edinburgh and Balfour gladly accepted seed of the beautiful hybrid *Gentiana* x *charpentieri*, the American lily *Helonias* and the Andean *Alstroemeria revoluta*. He was further delighted to have the 'best thing' that Bulley offered, which was a plant of the delicate Japanese *Shortia soldanelloides*. This was very rare then, and Bulley was as pleased as Punch that 'none of our nurserymen seemed to know that it was being offered.'

Bulley's letters were full of welcome surprises, because he had more freedom of manoeuvre than Balfour, and in 1896 he announced that he was sending a plant hunter to 'the Peloponnese to collect seeds and plants of that heavenly *Erodium chrysanthemum*.'[26] Some years before, Bulley had seen and coveted this plant in a Zurich nursery, loving its luminous, pale yellow flowers and its graceful, silvery, feathered leaves. But it was no longer available. Bulley also offered Balfour the seed of any other plants which could be collected from that expedition. As Balfour was in a government institution short of cash, this must have seemed wonderfully carefree. He lived in and for the botanic garden and his students, and it is no wonder that he warmed to a man who could write that 'the pleasure of having good things is giving them away'.

Bulley sent plants that Balfour had never seen, but which we now accept as part of our heritage. For example, when he sent the Russian sage, *Perovskia atriplicifolia*, with its aromatic, grey-green foliage and late-flowering blue flowers, Balfour nervously remarked, 'I hope we shall be able to succeed with it. I do not find anything about it in any of the gardening papers but I suppose that it will be fairly hardy coming as it does from the Himalayas.'[27] And it is.

In turn Balfour began to entrust precious seeds to Bulley's care. He sent him seed of several New Zealand species, including *Ranunculus buchananii* (found only in South Island) in order 'to double the chance of raising the crop'. It was a great compliment to Bulley's gardening skills, and he promised to do 'all which can be done for the Ranunculi seeds'. Balfour then asked if Bulley had any of the blue-flowered Himalayan poppies, and Bulley was absolutely delighted to receive *Meconopsis simplicifolia* and *M. aculeata*, these being 'plants which I have hunted everywhere'. A new gateway had opened through which Bulley was able to exchange plants and seeds of great rarity at that time.

For Bulley, too, it was wonderful to share his own enthusiasm, and to know that Balfour understood it. Bulley's love of beauty in flowers brims over in his letters. He would comment on the glorious colour of a flower or the wonder of its foliage. Or simply report the thrill of a recently discovered plant as 'flowering here a beauty'. This fine sense of appreciation fired Bulley's zeal to find other 'charmers' and to nurture them. This way he was always setting himself new challenges, and he got intense pleasure from this flow of absorbing thoughts and activities. The triumph of achievement in one new flower opening far outweighed the other disappointments, and once he had found a common bond with Balfour, he could share pleasures and problems with him in garden visits and correspondence. For example, when Bulley lost a precious plant of *Jankaea heldreichii*, he shared his sadness with Balfour, who only knew of one other plant in this country at the time. This beautiful flower grows wild on Mount Olympus in Greece, and it is protected today, but there were no such regulations a hundred years ago, and when Bulley managed to grow another, he wrote triumphantly, '*Jankaea heldreichii* is putting up a flower bud, and I am in the 7th heaven!'[28] Balfour replied 'Bravo *Jankaea*! Such moments are worth a lifetime.'[29]

The two men plainly enjoyed their correspondence, gradually becoming more gossipy, confidential and humorous. After a few years Bulley had the confidence to offer Balfour a plant which he confessed he did not want or like. It was *Panax crassifolia* from New Zealand and Bulley called it 'a sort of vegetable nightmare. It is a spindle shanked, angular, uncompromising, maiden aunt, abomination . . . I'll pack her off to you with joy, otherwise to the flames!'[30] Balfour relaxed, too, as if glad to be away from officialdom and enjoying some happy banter. He replied in similar vein, 'We are quite ready to flirt with your prude if you will give us the chance!'[31]

Bulley's rapture spilled over when two North American species were giving him particular pleasure:

> *Platystemon californicus* is wonderfully beautiful now. It is practically a perennial in my sandy soil, sowing itself freely. And the seedlings come through the hardest winter. Hanging over bits of loose wall, in crannies, or massed anywhere, the delicate sulphur yellow is in full sunshine a glorious sight which one cannot tire of. In the evening *Oenothera caespitosa*, covering yards of sandy rockery, perfumes the air, with its hosts of huge white flowers scented like a Daphne. [32]

They progressed from seed and plant exchange to reports of new techniques for plant growth. Bulley waxed eloquently on his successful oncocyclus irises, giving a detailed description of the dimensions of his wooden and glass frame, its sloping concrete base, its topping of gritty road scrapings and winter cover of straw, all producing 'flowers like nothing else in the wide world'. Balfour was so stimulated that he proposed 'at once to set about preparations for their cultivation' using Bulley's method, and he concluded, 'I appreciate your letters, full as they are of practical hints from which we cannot but benefit.'[33]

Bulley coaxed the less-hardy plants through the winter with infinite care. A peep at his garden in mid-winter revealed areas covered in coconut fibre, straw, bracken or glass, but hidden underneath were cosy corms, rhizomes and delicate buds which would erupt in late spring or early summer to produce a great show of glorious flowers such as those of the Californian poppy, *Romneya coulteri* and the bright blue hue of *Gentiana parryi*.

However, it was often a matter of trial and error. In those pioneering days in the growth of many newly introduced herbaceous and alpine plants, there were few precedents, no guide books, and no organisation with local groups for pooling information, as in the Alpine Garden Society today. This meant that an informal network of gardening friends was all the more valuable.

Sometimes Bulley would write in desperation to Balfour, if he was experimenting with a very choice plant, such as a rare ground orchid which is now protected by law. 'Can you do any good with *Cypripedium guttatum*? I lose it everywhere. It is Siberian so there ought to be no difficulty with it.'[34] Balfour was succeeding with a bud in a pot, but as this was only his first experience of the plant, he had no advice to offer. They were exploring together.

On the other hand, if he made a big mistake, Balfour would sometimes rescue him. When Bulley wrongly assumed that the beautiful blue gentian, *Gentiana ornata*, was a bog plant and 'put it where it can get its feet wet', he admitted the following spring that this gentian 'looks to me a deader', and received from Balfour not only advice but a new plant with which to try again!

No wonder that Bulley kept coming back for advice. When he noticed that Edinburgh was offering seeds of the spectacular *Phyteuma comosum* (syn. *Physoplexis comosa*) he asked, 'Did you artificially fertilise? The plant flourishes here but never seeds. I presumed the requisite moth with a long proboscis was wanting.'[35] He must have been having second thoughts because he knew this plant grows naturally in mountain limestone crevices, while Bulley was growing it on his sandstone rockery. Balfour confirmed that he fertilised his plants, but warned that a lack of hot summers in Britain often prevents ripening of 'many of the best things'.

When it came to soils, Bulley was particularly glad to swap news and views with a more experienced and up-to-date professional, because soil science was in its infancy. Gentians were his favourite flowers, because they 'excel in blue, my favourite colour' so their successful growth was particularly important to him. When he found *Gentiana parryi* and the difficult *G. ciliata* doing surprisingly well on his sandy rockery, which he had covered with a thick layer of granite chippings, he declared he was 'getting to be a wholesale believer in granite chippings'. Balfour replied 'Crushed granite is to my thinking a sort of "Bovril" or "Nestle's Food" for plants. I put it into almost every one of the soils in which I plant things in the Rock-Garden now. I take it the Potash of the Felspar is very grateful to most plants.'[36] So Bulley could continue reassured, until Balfour told him of the value of mica schist for mixing with loam, and he even sent him a sample of the micaceous soil from Ben Lawers, where so many alpine plants grow. Ben Lawers being so far from West Kirby, Bulley set about experimenting with a mixture of mica and quartz from Holyhead. Then Bulley became bitten with trying local burnt brick loam when he heard of its usefulness for alpines. Balfour followed suit. They were both willing to try anything new, with the hope of even greater success in their plants.

So the excellent relations continued, with Bulley's suggestions sometimes turning into urgent instructions: *Trollius calthaefolius* 'grab it' and the Turkish *Aethionema oppositifolium* 'collar it'. If both of them wanted a particularly choice plant, Bulley would try and think who might help, as he did for the tiny alpine, *Polemonium bicolor*, which he had previously obtained from Mt Rainier, in Washington State: 'Beloved of slugs. Gone also. Wonder whether Fairchild could get it.'[37]

Bulley's bubbling, free-flowing ideas and freedom of action helpfully contrasted with the steady, sound advice and scientific experience of Balfour. Their friendship was based on mutual respect and an amicable sharing of skills and experience, knowledge and ideas. It was a friendship which flourished through the ups and downs of life, and Bulley was enormously grateful. Sincerely felt thanks flowed from him, even if they were squeezed on the end of a tightly filled postcard, or on the back of an envelope, in the smallest handwriting and with inevitable abbreviations, as when Balfour had sent a parcel: 'Thanks for struck cuts of Gent.hex. [*Gentiana hexaphylla*]; for seeds I asked for; and indeed for constant mercies.'[38]

But Bulley came to a pivotal point: his gardening interests could not expand in West Kirby. There was no more room in his garden. Just as, on a larger scale, ever-bigger museums were being built in the 1890s to house the treasures gleaned during those days of Empire, so Bulley needed a bigger garden.

He began to search the Wirral and when he had found the best site, Balfour was one of the first people to know. When he was buying land in 1897, Bulley was flummoxed by the receipt of seeds from Yunnan which were far too precious to be put in jeopardy by an impending move. He sent Balfour the seed list and a special note: 'This letter discloses a little conspiracy against your peace ... My full and deadly purpose is to see if I can lure you into permitting me to share these seeds with you.'[39] Balfour obliged, 'Your conspiracy is a welcome one and we shall be most glad ...'

The bond between them was sealed in such crises. Bulley had a mentor of the highest calibre and an entrée to the expertise and facilities of the Royal Botanical Garden, Edinburgh. Their friendship was to be a key factor in the coming era of the great plant hunters in China and the Himalayas. It was a signpost pointing to Edinburgh as the headquarters for the identification of many of the newly discovered plants and the propagation of their seeds. Meanwhile Bulley had the joy of establishing his new gardens at Ness, where the propagation and merchandising of these seeds were also to take place.

3

Ness Gardens

*For the last 12 months I have been hunting for a site on which to build a
house and have an ideal garden. One has turned up recently with rock, sand,
clay, water and South slope. I think I shall very likely buy 5 or 10 acres ...*
(BULLEY, 1896).[1]

The land is bought

The years 1897–8 were a turning point in Bulley's life. These were the years in
which he bought farmland at Ness to create his gardens. It was an investment
which indicated his increasing commitment to horticulture, and it was a bold
and imaginative step which transformed his leisure life. It channelled his
creative energies, and later led him to harness his entrepreneurial spirit to the
commercial introduction of new and exotic flowers to Britain. It was a
personal step which was to become of national and international importance.

Bulley was probably alerted when the greater part of the township of Ness
was for sale by auction in Birkenhead on 21 July 1896. It was a rural area at a
time of agricultural depression and increased suburban spread, so it was
advertised as freehold building estate with easy access to Liverpool by road and
rail. A total of 778 acres (315 ha) were for sale in 51 lots of land.[2]

Bulley was familiar with the area; he had been to prep. school in nearby
Parkgate and since then he had often cycled, walked and searched for plants
there. This western side of the Wirral peninsula was still rural England, with
wonderful views to Wales across the Dee estuary. The field patterns had not
changed greatly since the tithe map was drawn in 1839, and many of the fields
and features were still known by their ancient names. Mickwell Brow means
'great spring at projecting edge of a hill', and pingo, from a local dialect word,
'pingot' means a small croft or enclosure of land. The undulating countryside
had an open, relatively treeless, windswept appearance, the fields dotted here
and there with ponds which had been dug for marl to improve the soil. Many
of the country families had lived there for generations, renting their few fields.
But there were collieries, too, by the shore of the River Dee, providing an extra
local income whilst a new railway station was planned at Burton Point,
enabling more potential commuters, like Bulley, to reside in the township.

Bulley had his eye on the sandstone spur, Mickwell Brow, as an ideal site on
which to build a house. The land there is 57 m above sea level, with steep

slopes on three sides. There was only a small clump of trees, so there were unimpeded, panoramic views of the Cheshire plain, the Dee estuary and the Welsh hills. But there was one big snag: at the auction the high ground was not for sale! It had been bought as an investment by a Liverpool architect, W A Thomas, three years earlier, before Bulley was ready to move from West Kirby. By 1896 there were still no houses on the hill, but Thomas looked set to build more than one property in the future, as at the 1896 Ness sale he snapped up the adjoining fields which made an excellent potential corner building site (Lot 15) with frontages to both Burton Road and Denhall Lane (see map). But Lot 15 was no good to Bulley without the adjoining hill top which was not for sale in 1896. Bulley bought no land at the sale itself.

But Bulley was a fighter. He and Mrs Bulley had now determined to move, a south-facing hill top was rare in Wirral, and this one could be combined with a garden ... maybe Bulley could buy out Thomas? There must have been family financial discussions that Christmas, especially with Bulley's eldest brother, Raffles. For 1897 proved to be a dramatic year, with leases and purchases of land at Ness far beyond the '5 or 10 acres' mentioned to Balfour just before Christmas 1896. There were negotiations with several different people, and the legal transactions lasted 18 months.

Thomas would not immediately sell all the land that Bulley wanted, but in March 1897 it was agreed that Bulley could have Lots 66 and 67 (see map), which consisted of over 12 acres (4.9 ha) bordering Burton Road including the hill top, Mickwell Brow, where Bulley wanted his house. Bulley paid £114 per acre. He also negotiated for two strips of land to the south (Lots 15A and 15B) at the lesser cost of £55 or £70 per acre. The narrowest strip was 40 feet (12 m) wide, so Bulley had the option of making a road or footpath to Denhall Lane, giving extra access and a short cut to the planned railway station at Burton Point. He must have been relieved and delighted. The land was legally his in July, and his brother-in-law began building the house. Progress was so rapid that the plan of the house was even shown on the 25-inch Ordnance Survey map the following year! Bulley also purchased Lot 12, 27 acres (10.9 ha) of lower land sloping down to the railway line. At £50 per acre it was a relatively cheap investment. He used a portion for a spinney, and rented the rest to local farmers.

Bulley's most intriguing acquisition was land called the Pingo. It belonged to a retired butcher from Everton, Mr Robert Maiden, who had inherited two small and separate pieces of land, the Pingo and Lampit, and it was agreed that they should both be leased to Bulley at a yearly rent of £20 'payable quarterly on the usual quarter days'. The pingo was conveyed in trust to Bulley's elder brother, Raffles, and leased to Bulley until the owner died, when it was agreed that Bulley could buy it ... The pingo was a small enclosure which comprised only 2 roods and 13 perches of land (0.24 ha), including a very deep pool of water, and a right of way to the Burton Road. This track remained a feature of the gardens for many years, and its route can still be picked out today, below the landscaped terraces. It officially enabled 'Thomas Raffles Bulley ... to pass

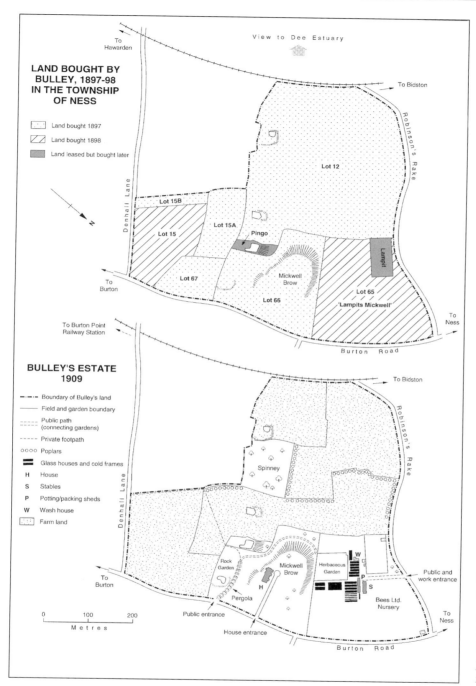

LAND BOUGHT BY BULLEY, 1897-98 IN THE TOWNSHIP OF NESS

Land bought 1897
Land bought 1898
Land leased but bought later

To Hawarden
View to Dee Estuary
To Bidston
Robinson's Rake
Denhall Lane
Lot 12
Lot 15B
Lot 15A
Pingo
Lampit
Lot 15
Lot 67
Mickwell Brow
Lot 66
Lot 65
'Lampits Mickwell'
To Burton
To Ness
To Burton Point Railway Station
Burton Road

BULLEY'S ESTATE 1909

— · — · — Boundary of Bulley's land
——— Field and garden boundary
- - - - - Public path (connecting gardens)
- - - - - Private footpath
oooo Poplars
Glass houses and cold frames
H House
S Stables
P Potting/packing sheds
W Wash house
Farm land

To Bidston
Robinson's Rake
Denhall Lane
Spinney
Rock Garden
Mickwell Brow
Herbaceous Garden
W
P
S
H
Pergola
Public and work entrance
Bees Ltd. Nursery
To Burton
Public entrance
House entrance
To Ness
Burton Road

0   100   200
Metres

(Top) *Land bought by Bulley, 1897–8, in the township of Ness.*

(Below) *Bulley's estate 1909. Source: deeds, Ordnance Survey maps, photos and people's memories.*

... with or without horses carts and carriages ... over and along a roadway leading ... from the high road.' Bulley always used this 'roadway' as a public path into his gardens, and in the early days it was covered by a rose-strewn pergola for most of its length, as seen on old photographs (see pp.48–9).

But Bulley still had two critically important purchases to make in order to complete his dream. To the north and adjoining Mickwell Brow, was a 10-acre

(4-ha) field, 'Lampits Mickwell' which would form an ideal corner to his estate, giving him a fairly flat stretch of land up to the lane, Robinson's Rake. This field belonged to Mr Barnes, a contractor from Lower Bebington, on the other side of the Wirral. But it had become clear to Bulley that this field would allow useful access, as a work entrance to the potential hub of the estate, where he could build stables, potting sheds and glasshouses. It would be well worth paying for. Bulley had to persuade Barnes to sell by offering over £122 per acre, more than twice what the contractor had paid for the field, and more than Bulley had paid per acre for all the other land. Then to purchase the last corner of land (the remainder of Lot 15), Bulley had to pay the architect, Thomas, £200 per acre, nearly two-and-a-half times the amount which Thomas has paid for it the previous year! However, on 17 August 1898 Bulley signed the final deeds to complete his compact estate of 60 acres (24 ha).

Altogether Bulley had invested £5525 in the land which was to become Ness Gardens, when a gardener's basic wage was only about £1 a week. It was an investment which he was never to regret. So as Queen Victoria's reign drew to its close, Ness Gardens began. The University of Liverpool bought an extra 2 acres (0.8 ha) in 1979, otherwise the gardens now fill the estate which Bulley established a century ago.

The Bulleys move in

The Bulleys moved into their new house in the autumn of 1898. It is difficult to imagine, now, how starkly it stood out on the hilltop, with only a small cluster of sycamores beside it. The house was built by Bulley's brother-in-law, Faulkner Armitage. There was no thought of a grandiose house, built to impress. It was functional, comfortable and built to last. For example, it stands on sandstone rock, but it is built of impermeable Ruabon bricks, hard and impenetrable to the elements; and the Bulleys chose modern, iron window frames and coke central heating with hot air ducts. It was also revolutionary, for those class-ridden times, in being designed with egalitarian thoughts towards the staff. It was orientated so that all the household could enjoy the maximum sunshine and views, the entrances from the drive being at the north-facing back of the house, leaving maximum south-facing window space. And the servants lived at the same level as the Bulleys.

An unusual 'King Cotton' had come to stay, an upstart to the gentry, a conundrum to the locals; a socialist landowner with high ideals and dreams of bringing garden flowers to the poor. These newcomers in the 'big house' must have intrigued everyone around as the acetylene lights beamed out across the fields from the curtainless windows.

The house and household were described by Augustine Henry while visiting the Bulleys in 1901. He started by saying 'The Bulleys are <u>very</u> [underlined twice] nice.'[3] He appreciated their simple lifestyle, lack of humbug, and freedom from upstairs-downstairs attitudes:

I am writing in the 'drawing-room'. It has two great windows, one at the end, one at the side: no curtains, no bric-a-brac, a low ceiling; shelves of books at the windowless end: writing table in a corner: a few engravings of good pictures (Watts e.g.), a living room in short, not a shop … There is a small dining-room equally plain, another sitting room: and beyond are the servants' '<u>drawing-room</u>', kitchen etc. – all on as big a scale as the owners' rooms. That is the two maids are very well-off indeed. Upstairs about 9 bedrooms not too large. There is a very roomy hall, where one can shake off, as it were rain and mud and get acclimatized, before going into the living rooms.

The Bulley's first child, Lois, with her German governess, by the main porch entrance of the north-facing back of house, October 1903.

Mrs Bulley, her face showing her sense of fun, October 1903.

He continued:

The meals are good and simple, very simple. Mr Bulley goes to bed at 9, is up at dawn. Breakfast is at 7.30 … Mrs Bulley is still in brown; she gets about two frocks every year, and hates to wear a hat; has long since given up gloves, at least in summer.

This letter was written only months before the Bulleys' first child was born, and if Henry had returned some years later he would have found two children, with a swing in the doorway and a tricycle in the passage, and a German governess whom they affectionately called 'Nenni' after Kipling's newly published *The Cat that Walked by Himself*. If he had stayed at a weekend he

would also have been treated to the music teacher playing on their new Bechstein full grand piano, perhaps accompanying Arthur Bulley's singing, as the children fell asleep upstairs to the sound of classical music.

The gardens evolve

Bulley planned to develop the land gradually, but his active mind was whirring with excitement. He asked to visit the Edinburgh Royal Botanic Garden to see their alpine plants, exchange ideas and 'gain words of wisdom' from Professor Balfour. His energy seemed unbounded, as he proposed to cycle up to Edinburgh in May or June, having visited Ireland in April to see the national botanic gardens at Glasnevin, and Smith's nursery at Newry. Balfour, knowing Bulley's love and enthusiasm for plants, wrote encouragingly to him, 'Your garden will become one of the finest Herbaceous and Alpine Gardens in the country.'[4]

Mr Bulley with Lois on his knee in the drawing room in 1902.

One of the first things that Bulley established were shelter belts, which were essential for protection from westerly gales. The original field boundaries were predominantly hawthorn intermixed with beech, ash and holly, and Bulley strengthened some of these by planting quick-growing Lombardy poplars, together with a spinney of mixed deciduous trees. Gradually more shelter was provided by holm oaks, a belt of wych elms, an oak wood (*Quercus palustris* and *Q. borealis* with *Davidia involucrata*) and a pine wood (see map opposite).

The south side of the house, 1905, showing the gorse-covered slopes and the long pergola which was the public entrance to the gardens.

The gardens were developed close to the base of the hill. And unlike many a country estate they were not designed to be integrated with the house. For, just as the Bulleys were breaking social barriers in their home, so they were doing a social experiment in their gardens. The gardens were always open to the public. So the hilltop was kept as the household preserve, private and surrounded by gorse-covered hillsides full of wildlife which the family loved to watch. And private footpaths radiated from the house to the gardens below.

Bulley used about 24 acres (10 ha) of the estate for gardening pursuits, but when the villagers talked about 'Bulley's Gardens' they were referring mainly to three separately enclosed gardens, each about an acre (0.4 ha) in size. These were linked by a public path which curved round the base of the hillside like a necklace with its carefully distributed gems. In the beginning the two main gems were the rock garden and the herbaceous garden, and they were on opposite sides of the hill. They were both begun by the turn of the century, and progress was so good that as early as March 1900 Bulley had no need of any of the plants on the seed list sent by the Edinburgh botanic garden. And in 1904, Bulley started a commercial nursery by the potting sheds. This became Bees Ltd and in the Edwardian era its catalogues often referred to his own gardens. Readers were shown photographs of his rockery and herbaceous borders, they were invited to catch a train to come and see them, or even to

Gardeners in the pergola, July 1905.

The full extent of 'Bulley's Gardens' in his lifetime. The separate gardens were linked by a public footpath, and recreation facilities were provided for local villagers. Source: Liverpool University archives, photos and people's memories.

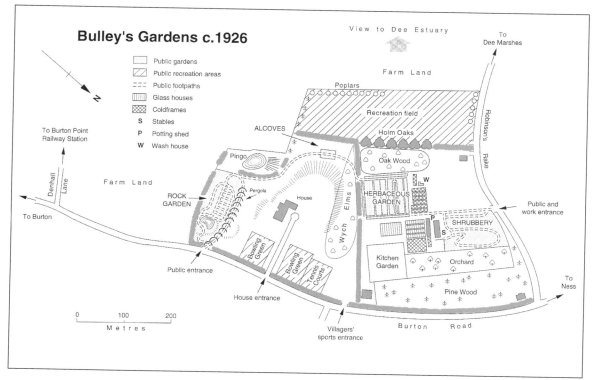

buy a collection of plants, and use plans prepared by Bees, so that they could have a border as good as his! It seems that it was after the First World War that a shrubbery, filled with new introductions of Forrest and Kingdon Ward, became an added and popular feature.

A spirit of experiment characterised Bulley's gardens, especially the rock garden. This was located south of the house, where marl workings had deepened the dell, marshy ground predominated, and ingenuity was needed to make the most of this sheltered, south-facing sun trap. But Bulley loved the challenge, and within the umbrella name of rock garden he dug a lily pond as a prime focus, experimented with raised beds, and tried the latest ideas of a moraine and a bog garden. The latter thrilled him so much that in June 1902 he advised the director of Kew to have one (neither Kew or Glasnevin botanic gardens had one at the time)!

Provision of a variety of soils and drainage within the rock garden was a major task and the whole area was developed over many years. Gravel chips were worked into the clay, and local people were encouraged to tip spare soil from their carts down a shute at the roadside. Old mortar provided cheap lime, and limestone was carted in from North Wales. One extensive scree is reported to have taken 50 cartloads of stones, and with no mechanisation it would take a day to drag two sandstone boulders from the hillside. The valley stream was diverted to make way for four raised, rectangular beds on which alpine plants flourished in a range of soils from lime-rich to peat-based, with leaf compost to help retain moisture where necessary. Later the most up-to-date sprinkler system was installed.

Bulley planted the beds densely, arranging plants so that one could shade another where necessary. And like William Robinson, he favoured large masses of alpine flowers, saying, 'a smaller number of first class kinds is much more effective than a large number of second class kinds.' He knew that the rockery enthusiast, Reginald Farrer, 'was dreadfully down on massing, which he thought smacked of the factory', but Bulley noted that 'Mother Nature does it herself on a huge scale. She does it with heather and bluebells and poppies and buttercups and broom, and hosts of other fine things. So that if I sin, I sin in good company, in fact with one of the best people, and that is always so dreadfully agreeable.'[5]

Many of Bulley's favourite plants were grown in the rock garden, and he found a niche for a huge variety. For example, he tried high alpine androsaces on the moraine, with *Campanula cenisia* and *C. alpestris*. He grew *Omphalodes luciliae* on a sunny raised bed, and *Haberlea rhodopensis* in a retaining wall by the stream, where sandstone blocks provided ideal vertical, moist and shady conditions. As he began to sponsor plant hunters, he added to the variety of plants. He loved the intense blue of the 'Grace Ward' variety of *Lithodora*, sprawling over rocks, and the tall heads of the Himalayan blue poppy, *Meconopsis betonicifolia* (Plate 24). He extended autumn flowering with *Crocus speciosus*, 'dainty and cool', and the striking *Gentiana sino-ornata* (Plate 20) collected by George Forrest. He tried them out in different places, 'I am always planning pictures in my mind ... not only for picturesque effect, but also for the health of the plants themselves.'[6] And a Bees' catalogue (1910–12) immodestly proclaimed 'Bees' Ravishing Rockeries', meaning Bulley's!

But as an Edwardian flower garden, Bulley's herbaceous garden must have been hard to beat. Located on the most suitable, deep-silt soil, displays of bedding and herbaceous borders provided seasonal bursts of colour which local people could hardly credit possible. An acre of a field was transformed, and the broad plan of the garden is shown (right). Along one side of the garden was an azalea border, backed by a hornbeam hedge, and this border has been retained, lengthened and broadened in recent times. At one end of the garden was a bright display of dahlias, and an area of rose beds of gentler hues. At the opposite end an iron trellis was covered in *Clematis montana*. Otherwise four monthly flower borders were Bulley's pride and joy. The May border was over 60 m long, on one side of the garden, while the June, July and August borders were across the garden. Bulley's method of constructing these three parallel, double borders, about 55 m long, was detailed in a Bees' catalogue (1910–12):

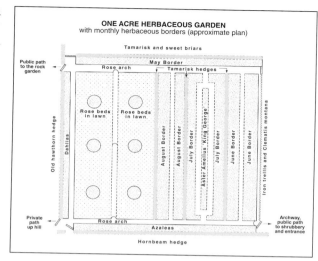

ONE ACRE HERBACEOUS GARDEN
with monthly herbaceous borders (approximate plan)

> We dug out three miniature river beds. None of the three to the same depth or the same plan. The bottom we made into a path. Some of the paths wriggle; some don't. We threw the soil right and left, but omitted to make the sides like the roof of a house. We left them rather lumpy in places, with the result that we can secure a good wavy contour without calling too frequently on the stronger-growing plants.

Having ensured a good topsoil, an informal planting plan was made, grouping plants for effect. The cinder paths, edged with stones, were over 1 m wide, wide enough for a gardener's cart, or for two people to walk comfortably side by side and admire the banks of flowers. The flower borders were between 3 and 4 m wide on either side, backed by a tamarisk hedge. The banks of flowers were so high that no one could be seen across them, and people could sit on benches to 'soak up' the glorious sight of one month's blooms at a time.

The May border is the only one described in detail:

> Cottage and Darwin tulips, carpeted with dwarf Arabis, Phlox, Aubretia, Forget-me-nots, Gentians, Primroses, Violets etc. and interspersed with

(Top) *The double herbaceous borders were featured in Bees' catalogues as a showpiece. They were enjoyed for over 50 years before their deterioration in the Second World War led to new landscaping. Source: Ken Hulme et al.*

(Below) *The double August border being quietly enjoyed by members of the household. A 1912 Bees' caption was: 'He who hath two loaves, sell one and buy anemones, for flowers are the food of the soul.'*

‘St Bruno’s’ and other Lilies, Snowflakes, Sun Spurge, Geums … [with]
well placed Flowering Brooms, Genistas, Peonies, Fritillaries, Camassias …
and Maples. The background is of Hybrid Sweet Briars, against the
incomparable feathery tamarisk.

When the early-flowering bulbs had ripened, seeds of annuals were then
sown, and spare plants inserted, to gain a second crop of flowers and ‘a new
phase of beauty’.

Imagine a walk round the hillside when the gardens had matured in the
1920s. From the public entrance on the Burton Road, a pergola provided a
delightful covered walk overlooking the rock garden, and leading along the
ancient track to the pingo. There were a hundred kinds of roses trained up
wooden poles with clematis and scented wisteria. Visitors could digress into
the rock garden and admire the alpine flowers, picnic by the pool where the
weeping willows overhung the water, or continue past the pingo where
plantings of *Leucojum aestivum* gave a spot of cultivated wildness in spring.
Walking round the hillside, wildlife abounded. The mixture of brambles and
bracken, rough grassland and gorse was home to badgers, foxes and rabbits,
and alive with linnets, greenfinches and a kingfisher which caught sticklebacks
in the pond to feed its young. The path wound through the shade of sycamores
into a grassy field, and near the present heather garden a gate opened into a
walled garden where the weary could sit in alcoves of seats, tucked into the
hillside. The dry stone walls were planted with alpines such as *Iris stylosa* which
Bulley described as having ‘the gracious characteristic of flourishing best when
on the verge of starvation’. But people fortified by rest would leave this
seclusion and soon find themselves entranced by the herbaceous garden.

Behind the hornbeam hedge, the nursery of Bees Ltd no longer existed in
the 1920s, having been moved to Sealand, near Chester. But the private area of
the garden included plentiful produce for the ‘big house’ and the people of
Ness. There were glasshouses with cucumbers and tomatoes, peaches and
plums, chrysanthemums and orchids. There were meticulously cordoned fruit
trees with gooseberries and peas interplanted with them, and a huge cage for
soft fruit - strawberries, raspberries, redcurrants. There were sweet peas and
roses for cutting and vegetables for all the year. Propagation of rare and new
plants continued, and trial beds where ‘Mr Bulley used to go round; if he liked
them he’d keep them, if he didn’t like them, he’d throw them away.’[7]

But the public would pass this by and enter the shrubbery, a sheltered area
where many newly introduced rhododendrons were planted. The maze of
paths also brought one close to the beautiful hybrid *Rhododendron* ‘Loderi’, the
fragrant *Magnolia sieboldii* and *M. salicifolia* and *Pieris formosa forrestii* (Plates 4 and 5)
which all grow there today.

The gardeners

Such gardens are not made by singing: ‘Oh, how beautiful,’ and sitting in
the shade.[8]

In December 1896, before even an acre of land at Ness was his, Bulley was looking for gardeners. It was his hallmark that he sought good advice. To obtain key gardeners he did not rely on adverts in gardening papers, which gave 'swarms of men … with unexceptional testimonials.' He wrote personally to top men at the Royal Botanic Gardens of Edinburgh and Kew, who knew their trainees, and had many contacts. His instinct was first to write to Professor Balfour and if unsuccessful, Bulley tried for someone from Kew. For his first senior gardener at Ness, Bulley explained his requirements to Balfour: 'As you know, he will have the care of some very out of the way things, and will have to use his head in the culture of difficult subjects.' He always checked what he should pay his new employee, to give him a fair wage - or above this if he wanted him badly! This way Bulley obtained some exceptionally keen and talented men. They also gained invaluable experience which contributed to their careers.

The first head gardener had to oversee a huge workforce, as the potting shed and glasshouses were built, herbaceous borders dug and the rock garden begun – without any machinery. They used wheel barrows, carts, pulleys and rollers to transport boulders and soil round the garden. Compost-making was a mammoth task. Using a horse and cart, and later a Ford T truck, peat was dug and collected from nearby woods, leaves were gathered along country lanes, manure was heaped in the midden – and all mixed with loam and sand in different proportions for different plants. By 1907, when Bees' Nursery was established in the garden, Bulley was employing 52 garden staff, with a wage bill of £50 a week. The head gardener was paid 30s a week with a 'good cottage'. (The average weekly wage earnings were 28s for men in manufacturing at the time.) Eight of the gardeners were on a basic wage of between 25 and 30s a week, whilst the other workers' wages ranged from a basic 21s down to 5s a week for 6 days' work.[9] Many of them were local but some even came from the continent, to which they later returned with local brides.

Bulley's success in getting good men can be seen by their subsequent careers. An early head gardener, L G Godseff, went on to a post with Liverpool Corporation. Bulley felt bereft when he left in 1903: 'He was a gem, and I feel destitute in his loss.'[10] But they kept contact and when Bees Ltd was established,

The garden staff in 1905, including lads who left school at 12 years old.

Mr Josiah Hope, aged 88 years, when he had been associated with Ness Gardens for over 50 years.

orders came from Liverpool parks, where Godseff became director. There is a *Saxifraga* X *elizabethae* var. 'Leo Gordon Godseff' named after him.

When starting Bees' Nursery, Bulley sought a man 'skilful in propagation, apt for organisation, and with a range of experience.' He found A J Macself, who later became editor of *Amateur Gardening*, and then John Besant, who later became director of Glasnevin, Ireland's premier botanical garden.

Bulley's longest-serving head gardener was Josiah Hope. He came at a critical point in 1913, when Bulley was awaiting seed collected in China by Frank Kingdon Ward. Bees' Nursery was being transferred to Sealand, near Chester, and Bulley was looking forward to expanding his ornamental gardens and plant hybridisation at Ness. He would need expert help. Excitement coloured his request to Balfour in January 1913: 'Can you give me someone good to take charge of my garden and greenhouses here? ... I am not particular about wages if you can send a good man.'[11]

Bulley must have been delighted at his good luck. Josiah Hope, the head herbaceous foreman at the Royal Botanic Garden, Edinburgh, was interested in a new job with better pay. Balfour wrote: 'You get a rattling good man and he will be a loss to us, but under our present regime I have not been able to squeeze more than a maximum of 39s a week for men of his position and so we have to part with them when better opportunities offer.'[12] Bulley offered 45s a week, removal expenses and the promise of accommodation. Hope arrived at the end of February 1913, with his wife and two young children.

Hope had impeccable credentials in training, experience and character. He had been an apprentice at the famous nursery in York of James Backhouse, who was a pioneer of building rock gardens for alpine plants, when such plants were scarcely to be found outside botanic gardens. He had worked in the hardy plant department of the botanic garden, Cambridge, and on several large estates before he became foreman of alpine, rock garden and herbaceous plants in the famous garden of Sir Edmund Loder, at Leonardslee, Sussex. Most recently, he had even propagated plants collected by George Forrest, Bulley's first professional plant hunter. No wonder Bulley and Hope got on well! Moreover, he had studied hard, gaining two RHS certificates in horticulture; his testimonials spoke of his steady industry, obliging, pleasant manners and good character. Hope was Conservative in politics and a mason, but the two men respected each other's honest opinions, and in the propagation of new and rare hardy and alpine plants, they were a rare match.

Hope was particularly keen on hybrid primulas, and Bulley happily reported to Balfour, 'We are in daily discussion here re your paper on Propagation in the Journal ... I am watching Hope's practice most closely.'[13]

Two months later he described the fun they were having: 'A seedling is in flower here which must be a cross between *P. bulleyana* (Plate 11) and *P. cockburniana*. It is simply wonderful. We have no knowledge of having made a cross; but we are making it now.'[14] So began a flourishing gardening partnership of nearly 30 years.

There were dramatic moments, when the two men nearly came to blows. On one occasion, Bulley wanted to verify the name of a plant grown from Kingdon Ward's seed, by sending it to Balfour: 'I enclose herewith a flower and a leaf. (I tried to get the whole plant for you; but Hope suggested that it would then be necessary for him to commit suicide!)'[15] Hope also drove his men hard; those were disciplined days and there were times when they 'couldn't straighten their backs' to stop and have a drink. They worked until 1 p.m. on Saturday, and there was no leaving early … they had to bound down the lane to catch the 1.10 p.m. train to watch a Liverpool football match.

A bell on the gable end of the stables signalled the strict daily timetable – and Hope's wrath was brought down on any latecomer! Work began at 8 a.m. until 12.15 p.m., then 1.15 p.m. until 5 or 5.30 p.m., depending on the season. At the end of a work session the bell was rung twice, first for the tools to be put away, and five minutes later to signal the time to go home. One day Bulley found that a deaf-and-dumb girl did not realise that the bell had rung, so he went up to her, put out his left palm, and 'wrote' on it with one finger, ''op it!' In the early days people walked or cycled, but after the First World War a bus was provided – and a bath for those without one at home.

Will Ingwersen, the alpine expert, could remember being in awe of Hope when he visited Ness Gardens as a child. But once Hope realised that Will was a real plant lover, and knew the name of that great alpine rarity from New Zealand, *Raoulia eximea*, Hope's kindness shone through. Will enjoyed several more visits, finding Hope a store of plant knowledge.[16]

It was fortunate that Josiah Hope did not have to leave Ness Gardens during the First World War. He was called up three times, but Bulley's astuteness came to the rescue. Each time he wrote that Hope was needed to grow food as part of the war effort. Hope was exempted from military service and wheat was grown behind the stables. Hope was made a special constable, and continued to grow plants from new seed sent by Bulley's collectors. After the war Bulley arranged for Hope, too, to go plant collecting in the Alps.

Bulley realised his debt to Hope and when one of his hunters, Cooper, found a new plant in the Himalayas, Bulley wrote to Balfour, in 1917: 'I should be quite glad to have Hope's name on the white sikkimensis-like Primula. He grew and flowered it and would, I am sure, much appreciate the compliment.'[17] Balfour replied: 'Dear Mr Bulley, Certainly I shall name the plant *Primula hopeana*.'[18] But the name did not last long; it was decided that it was only a variety of a variable species, and is now called *P. sikkimensis* var. *hopeana*. Later, when Kingdon Ward introduced a new gentian, it was called *Gentiana hopei*, and given an award of merit at the Chelsea Show in 1923.[19] It is now called *G. trichotoma* (Plate 21) but there is still a variety of *Clematis* called 'J. Hope', which bears large blush-pink flowers in July and August. When Bulley died, Mrs Bulley wrote her own personal tribute, too, to 'the loyal co-operation of Mr Hope, his head gardener'. She followed this by putting Hope's name forward for the prestigious 'Associate of Honour' which is awarded by the RHS to those 'who have rendered distinguished service to horticulture in the course of their employment.'

A fine core of the workforce also gave long and loyal service to the gardens; some local people came straight from school and spent a large part of their lives in the gardens. Bill Cottrell was born in Ness and worked in the gardens for over 50 years. He tended them with care and pride, and when, in later years, he sat on the glacial boulder and reflected on the past, he surveyed the scene and said 'Me and 'ope made this Rock Garden.'[20] Henry Vincent joined him, and his son and daughter-in-law are still on the staff. Indeed, father and son, Henry and Keith Vincent, have each been awarded a Royal Horticultural Society medal for completing 40 years of unbroken service at Ness.

Hannah Smith (née Jones) has happy recollections of working in the gardens for 5s a week in the 1920s. Her mother was a cleaner in the 'big house' and Hannah joined the garden staff on leaving school. She can remember with pride having a brown uniform fitted in Liverpool, made of corduroy in winter, cotton drill in summer; knee breeches and a jacket-overall and black stockings. She started in the potting shed making compost and cleaning pots, stoking the fire and feeding the cats, which were kept to keep down the mice. She watered cuttings every two hours, and tidied up the chrysanthemums. Later she worked in the rock garden, until the cotton slump sadly forced Bulley to lay off staff. She recalls that Bulley knew his staff by their first names, and as he walked around, a slightly bent figure with his hands clasped behind his back, he would stop for a kindly word, but if there was a stray convolvulus weed in the rockery, 'He'd bring you from one end of the gardens to the other to dig it up!' She also remembers Sunday outings to Bees' Nursery and North Wales, being given a bunch of chrys-anthemums at Christmas, and when she (Hannah) was married, Mrs Bulley gave her a five pound note – 'a big white one'.

The Bulleys had a good relationship with all their staff; there was a feeling of mutual respect, summed up in the phrase of one former gardener: 'Mr Bulley was a nice Gentleman.'

Women gardeners, Hannah Jones (left, now Mrs Smith) and Susie Swift (now Mrs Palmer), wearing their brown uniform and black stockings, gathering Michaelmas daisies about 1931.

Sharing the gardens

> Welcome friend and welcome stranger!
> Welcome one and welcome all.

So sang Bulley at Ness, from the words of his old school song. And he put the words into practice. The Bulleys' philosophy was to share, and they shared their garden with the community in a most outstanding way, and far ahead of their times. There had been nothing like this in Ness before! If there had been some resentment when the house was first built because it occupied a favourite picnic spot, this soon evaporated when jobs became available and when a green noticeboard on a gate at each end of the gardens announced in gold letters that everyone was welcome to come in. Children had to be accompanied and dogs kept on a leash, but every day except Christmas Day they could enter freely from dusk until dawn.

The Bulleys had a Victorian ethic of public service, and a commitment to the ideal of social harmony. Bulley had written in his political notebook, 'Self help must give way to communal help', and in opening their garden he hoped, too, that the joy of gardening would spread. And they were well prepared for visitors. There were numerous benches and seats around the garden, and by each one was an upturned, 6–8-inch (15–20-cm) earthenware pipe, painted green and waiting for cigarette ends and litter. There were toilets, and a drinking fountain where people could 'water up' by pressing the brass button and catching the refreshing cold water in the iron cup which was hanging by a chain. Rare or isolated plants were kept well away from any intending thief, and the immensely loyal garden staff would let no one pull out a plant or pinch a pear; if a local lad was suspected of this by a faithful retainer, Bill Cottrell, he would check the soles of the lad's shoes against the offending footprint!

'Bulley's gardens' became so popular that postcards were printed showing glimpses of picturesque parts like the weeping willows overhanging the rock garden pool. And Bulley himself got 'tremendous dividends of happiness' by seeing everyone's enjoyment. As an old man he wandered incognito amongst visitors and chuckled at what he heard; but every now and then he would get exceptional pleasure from overhearing someone who understood the difficulties he had surmounted, as when he once heard 'Think of the brain behind it!'

Many young gardeners at Ness were amazed at the Bulleys' 'great big kitchen garden' but they shared in some of that, too. Sacks of apples and pears were left at the bus stop for people to help themselves, and all the village children had an apple with an orange and a shilling at Christmas – when a shilling bought a good-quality pair of woollen socks. Sometimes the sharing of the garden was unofficial, as when scoots' (moorhens') eggs were eaten, or when in times of local hardship and wartime meat rationing, rabbit pies were appearing on local folks' tables from the use of secret snares, ferrets and even a gun at break of dawn.

Bulley's special thrill was in sharing the pleasure of the rare plants in his garden with other expert gardeners and alpine plant enthusiasts. A member of a local amateur gardeners' association, Charles Pearson, of New Brighton, wrote several notes in his diary referring to visits between 1901 and 1912. He travelled by train on a Saturday afternoon, and on 1 September 1901 he recorded, 'Went with Amateur gardeners to Burton to visit the garden of Mr A.K. Bulley, who is a great specialist particularly in rare plants. A very fine aft. & a most enjoyable visit.' And on 5 September 1903, 'Joined Am. gardener's picnic to Mr Bulley's garden at Burton ... most enjoyable ... seeing the plants & having them explained.'[21] Bulley would often add some dramatic note to a tour of his garden. Another visitor recalled him saying of a *Rosa rugosa*, 'That rose bush is doomed to an early death. It will be smothered by the leaves of Clematis 'Gloire de St. Julien'. But I shall let the massacre go on, for I love that Clematis second to none.'[22]

Bulley exchanged visits, plants and ideas in an informal horticultural network which extended across Europe to America. In England he visited the gardens of famous contemporaries such as Gertrude Jekyll and William Robinson, and was visited by other great plantsmen and women from Walter Ingwersen to Ellen Willmott. And his eyes must have positively twinkled on receiving a letter addressed to 'The Owner, The Garden of Eden, Wirral'!

This link with the Garden of Eden would not have been lost on Bulley. He would have known from his boyhood in chapel that 'The Lord God planted a garden eastward in Eden' (*Genesis* 2 v 8). The medieval 'Mappa Mundi' in Hereford Cathedral even shows the Garden of Eden on an offshore island of China! As Bulley hired plant hunters to go to China, bringing back a bounty of flower seed, the link between the 'Garden of Eden' and his gardens was particularly apt.

Part II

Bulley's Plant Hunters
in the Sino-Himalaya

4

George Forrest and Bees Ltd

There are few things in the wide world I should enjoy more
than sending out a collector (BULLEY, c.1897). [1]

Context of rivalry

A new era was opening for Bulley as the twentieth century began. As his gardens at Ness expanded, he seemed ready to fulfil a greater public role in the gardening world. He had joined an RHS committee on the cultivation of new hardy plants, he was publishing his new plant introductions, and new possibilities were being mulled over in his mind. In 1899, Messrs Veitch Nurseries in London had sent out a gardener, Ernest H Wilson, to collect new plants and seeds in China. Should Bulley follow suit? The idea brought a competitive thrill, heightened by ideals of serving his country and its botanical institutions. Yet he hesitated. It was a big step to take. He would need a nursery to cover expenses and Bulley could not contemplate this yet. It was not long since he had moved house; his gardens were embryonic, and his finances insufficient.

Augustine Henry's visit to Ness in 1901 came at an ideal time. A great authority on Chinese plants, Henry had helped Wilson in China. Henry was keen to persuade Bulley, too, to have his own collector and Bulley asked about the best locations for future garnerings. They walked and talked along the sands of the Dee estuary.

Bulley knew that a Manchester friend had opened a more direct route to Yunnan. On 3 March 1900, he had written to Balfour in Edinburgh, 'My best news is that my friend Hobson of the Chinese Customs is on his way to open Teng Yueh on the Burma Chinese border, and within hail of the Delavay Country.'[2] The French missionary, Abbé Delavay, had discovered many new species, so Bulley was delighted that his friend was 'going to collect seeds vigorously, and should bag some good things.' But was this enough for Bulley? After all, he had counselled the RHS that only systematic and trained collecting was of any value. But still Bulley held back from sending a professional collector.

Meanwhile, Bulley had heard that the Imperial Russian Geographical Society was sending an expedition to south-east Tibet, and instinctively he asked for seed. The Russian explorer, Captain Koslov, was in command. The expedition set off in 1899, and after crossing the Gobi Desert, they went southwards and collected seed from a valley of one of the headwaters of the Mekong river. The expedition returned in 1901, and Bulley received seeds via the Imperial Botanic Garden of St Petersburg.

The seeds included *Meconopsis*, a genus of poppies, or poppyworts, that Bulley admitted he was 'mad on'. He had grown several Himalayan species. He was one of the first gardeners in Britain to experiment with *Meconopsis bella* and to produce flowers of *Meconopsis grandis*, so it was with relish that he sowed the Koslov seeds. As the plants grew he put some outdoors and others indoors, waiting to see if they would flower.

Then a coincidence occurred that turned into hot rivalry. In January 1903, the firm of Veitch despatched Wilson on a second expedition to China for the sole purpose of introducing the gorgeous yellow poppywort, *Meconopsis integrifolia* (Plate 1), the lampshade poppy. It is the largest-flowered species of *Meconopsis*, a plant to cherish. These yellow poppies had been described by a Russian, Przewalski, 30 years before, and more recently they had been reported growing in the alpine pastures above Tachien-lu (Kangding), near the Tibetan border. That was where Wilson was going so that he could be the first person to introduce them to Britain. He found them in July 1903, and marvelled at their large, globular, clear yellow blossoms, with their tissue-paper-thin petals. He collected abundant seed which he immediately sent back to Veitch in triumph.

No one knew that Bulley already had seeds of this plant at Ness! His Koslov seeds had included this species. He was about to spring an awful surprise on the venerable firm of Veitch. He decided late in 1903 that he would start his own nursery, A Bee & Co, and a superb opening gambit would be to advertise this plant in the catalogue!

The year 1904 was one of great excitement. One of the outdoor plants at Ness flowered. It was a rapturous moment. Bulley thought he was the first to grow it in Europe. His head gardener, William Coutts, announced the good news in the *Gardeners' Chronicle* on 17 September 1904. 'This plant is now in flower in Messrs Bee's nursery at Neston, and although the flower is 4 inches across, the plant itself has more the appearance of an alpine plant ... it is expected to prove a perennial ...'[3] Bulley had scored a coup!

Not knowing how long the flower would last, Bulley sent urgent messages to his secretary's sister, Mary Wroe, in Manchester, to come and paint this very special flower. He contacted William Robinson, and the painting was published, as a full plate colour illustration (Plate 1), in Robinson's new gardening journal, *Flora & Silva*.[4] It was marvellous publicity before advertising it in Bees' first catalogue of hardy plants (March 1905). His fledgling nursery, then 'The Co-operative Bees, Ltd', had a section on 'novelties' and plants of *Meconopsis integrifolia* were sold for the expensive sum of 10s 6d (the cost of a good pair of shoes).

The announcement of Bulley's flower produced horror and pique in the nurseries of Messrs James Veitch & Sons, Chelsea. It was as if a small, young, northern upstart of a nurseryman, David, was challenging the elder, established city Goliath. And the challenge hit a sensitive spot, as Veitch had sent Wilson a costly 13 000 miles especially to hunt for this flower! The following week it was announced that Veitch, too, had 'plants raised from seeds sent home by their special collector, E H Wilson, who is at present in Western China.' Then Veitch attempted deliberately to diminish Bulley's achievement by a published extract from one of Wilson's letters concerning *Meconopsis integrifolia*: 'I have nothing but success to report. I have found it in millions.'[5] Further, to 'outdo' Bulley, Veitch's plant was portrayed in the élite *Curtis's Botanical Magazine*.

In public, Bulley was undeterred. He obtained some of Messrs Veitch's plants, observed that they were not exactly the same as his, and sent one of his remaining plants to Prain at Kew for confirmation of identification, just in case it was another new species![6] For some years, indeed, it was thought that the differences merited a separate name for Bulley's plant, *Meconopsis pseudointegrifolia*.[7] Eventually, when many more plants had been collected from intervening areas, it was decided that the plants represented merely regional variations within a wide distribution.

In private, the Wilson introduction was a blow, both in itself and because Wilson and Veitch gained more publicity and recognition. Even 30 years later Charles Elliott remembered the sensation this lovely plant made when the House of Veitch first showed it at one of the Temple Shows. Wilson's large haul caused such rejoicing in the Veitch camp, that Wilson was given an amazing tie pin, fashioned like a yellow poppywort, with petals of gold and 40 stamens made of diamonds! This is the last thing that Bulley would ever have wanted. What disappointed him was the lasting public impression that Wilson was the winner in the race to introduce *Meconopsis integrifolia*. After all, Bulley was growing the seed before Wilson ever found the plant, and Bulley was first to the post in publication.

Years later, the incident still rankled Bulley. A 1912 Bees' catalogue, advertising *Meconopsis integrifolia*, stated 'We may rightly claim to have first introduced this magnificent Poppy to this country ...'

However, Veitch had had the advantage of a professional collector with abundant fresh seed. That was enormously helpful in ensuring the long-term introduction of the plant. Bulley knew it. Indeed, Bulley had his own professional plant collector already on his way to Yunnan, when he broke the good news of his *Meconopsis integrifolia* in 1904. Moreover, Balfour was to call his new plant collector the 'Prince of Collectors', and he was to collect many more new species over the next 27 years.

At last Bulley had made the crucial decisions, to have his own nursery and his own collector. Now he could rival Veitch on more equal terms. A dream was born.

One enabling factor must have been more money. In the early 1900s, there was an enormous volume of cotton being traded. It was possible to make very profitable manoeuvres in Liverpool, in speculative exchange, dealing in futures on the New York Cotton Exchange. It would be surprising if such a wily man had not managed it! What is certain is that Bulley eventually heeded Augustine Henry's constant advice: 'Don't waste money on postage. Send a man!' [8]

My beastly money

Royal Botanic Garden
Edinburgh
28 April 1904

Dear Mr Bulley

There is a man, Forrest, here who is on the look out for a billet such as you describe. I have given your letter to him and he will write to you … He has been working here for about 6 months and I have found him an excellent industrious and steady man. He has had opportunity here of getting to know a good deal about the plants of the world and he seems to have profited by it. The Head of the Herbarium speaks very highly of him. He is a strongly built fellow and seems to me to be of the right grit for a collector.

Yours very truly,
Isaac Bayley Balfour [9]

(Below) *Arthur Bulley writes for a reference for George Forrest before hiring him as a plant hunter for his nursery.*

What wonderful news! By return of post Bulley asked for more details, and had a reassuring response:

Forrest should be all right in the way of health, honesty, steadiness, devotion to work, general knowledge of plants. Of his gardening powers I know nothing; he has not been on our gardening staff. I should say that if he knew what you want he would do well for you. [10]

It was April 1904, a turning point in the lives of Bulley and George Forrest. They were about to enter into a contract which was to lead to one of the most adventurous and productive plant-hunting expeditions that there has ever been in China.

The expedition had the full support and co-operation of Balfour and his team at the Royal Botanic Garden, Edinburgh. Having no money for exploration, they delighted in the link with Bulley's enterprise. Balfour wanted dried plant specimens and seeds. Bees Ltd would grow and market the seeds. Bulley, like Blake, could see 'a Heaven in a Wild Flower', [11] but now he also had the scent of profit!

Forrest was just 31 years old. He was a Scot, born in Graham's Road, Falkirk, the son of a draper's assistant. He had already 'roughed it' in the Australian bush, but now he was living with his widowed mother on the outskirts of

Plate 9.
Primula vialii,
introduced by Forrest from
Yunnan, was an early
award winner. It was one
of the plants Bulley tried
on Snowdon.

(*Above right*) **Plate 12.**
Primula florindae,
*discovered by Ward in Tibet
in 1924.*

(*Below*) **Plate 13.**
'*Candelabra*' *hybrids
flourishing at Harlow Carr.*

(*Facing page*) **Plate 10.**
*Bees' first colour catalogue
picture (1911). Primula
'Unique' was a cross between
P. cockburniana and
P. pulverulenta.*

(*Above left*) **Plate 11.**
*Primula bulleyana,
discovered by Forrest in
Yunnan and introduced
through Bees Ltd, was an
immediate success.*

Plate 14.
Bees' logo in 1910. Bulley often described his staff as 'Busy Bees', and plants were named after his nursery.

(Left) **Plate 15.**
Jasminum beesianum.

(Below left) **Plate 16.**
Allium beesianum in Yunnan.

(Below right) **Plate 17.**
Rhododendron beesianum in Yunnan.

Edinburgh. He was a keen naturalist, he loved the hills, and he was so fit that he walked six miles to and from work and stood in the herbarium all day. He became engaged to a Miss Clementine Traill, whom he had met in the herbarium, but he was still ripe for adventure, and yearned to be a plant hunter. He agreed to go for two years, and within a month he was sailing on the SS *Australia* bound for Rangoon.

Bulley sent him to collect seeds of alpine and hardy herbaceous plants from the high plateau and mountain ranges of north-west Yunnan, an area south and west of Wilson's main hunting ground. Yunnan, whose name means 'south of the clouds', contains the extraordinary phenomenon of the three immensely deep gorges of the Salween, Mekong and Yangtze rivers. These three mighty

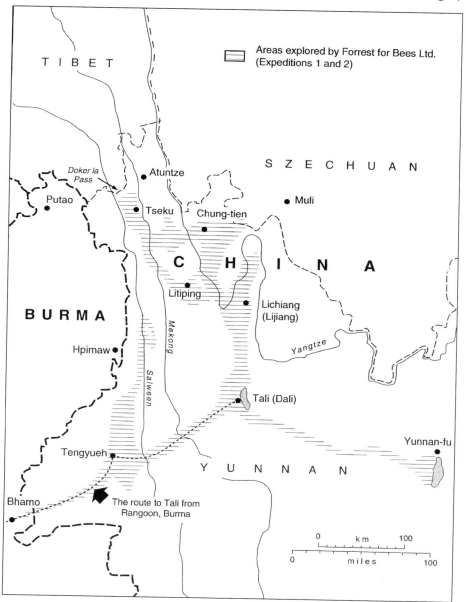

North-west Yunnan, China, the mountainous hunting ground of George Forrest. The names are those used by him and contemporary plant hunters. Source: Royal Botanic Garden, Edinburgh.

The town of Tali / Talifu: a photograph by George Forrest, who often stayed here and hunted for plants on the nearby mountains (Cang Shan). It was also a staging post for Kingdon Ward.

George Forrest (1873–1932) relaxing in camp in Yunnan.

rivers flow from the snowy, windswept heights of the Tibetan plateau and are parallel for nearly 200 miles, separated by high mountains, only 50 miles apart. The Yangtze then turns through 180 degrees and winds its way spectacularly through northern Yunnan, in a generally easterly direction, eventually to reach the Pacific near Shanghai. The other two rivers continue south; the Salween through Burma to the Indian Ocean, and the Mekong through Vietnam to the South China Sea.

George Forrest's photograph of his camp in the Lichiang Range (Yulongshan), north-west Yunnan. Piles of drying plants and paper are in the foreground.

Forrest soon started a reconnaissance, heading 200 miles east of Tengyueh across a rolling plateau to Abbé Delavay's favourite range of snow-capped mountains west of Tali (sometimes referred to as Talifu). This historic walled town, which was visited by Marco Polo centuries earlier, was to be a base for Forrest's fertile collections in the Tali (Cang Shan) mountains.

He set off with his Winchester gun, porters and mules loaded with plant presses, camping equipment, his stock of medicines and spare supplies of rice. Plants were collected from a near-tropical altitudinal zone in the sheltered, deep valleys, up through temperate, cool temperate, sub-alpine to alpine conditions over 4900 m above sea level.

He hunted plants from limestone cliffs to dense forests, from rocky ledges and crevices to boggy, peaty ground. Each plant was pressed dry in paper, given a 'Forrest' number, corresponding to numbered notes containing a description of the plant, its habitat, locality, latitude, longitude and altitude. Seeds were sorted, dried, given a number and packaged in small envelopes. It all demanded painstaking care and organisation.

Meanwhile, the bigwigs of the RHS were enjoying much pomp and circumstance in London. On Friday, 22 July 1904, their new hall was formally opened by His Majesty King Edward VII. Few people probably knew that a young man, George Forrest, was on his way to collect new seed in China. Certainly the RHS itself had been far too busy raising money for the hall, to contemplate sending out its own collector. But, thanks to Bulley's initiative, the seeds that Forrest collected were to produce highlights at shows in the London hall for years to come, and were to change the face of gardening.

Bulley was busy experimenting with new plants as usual. He was carefully mulching an American alpine from Mt Rainier, *Lupinus lyalli*, and being frustrated by Calcutta seed of *Meconopsis bella*. The more it frustrated him, the more he wanted to triumph. 'If I get seed again I shall try mulching the seed pan surface with powdered charcoal. I got one seedling to 5 leaves ...'[12]

Eager to prepare more ground for his nursery and future Forrest plants, he made an urgent request to the director at Kew, 'Can you perchance give me the name of any maker of steam diggers? I have a pile of digging to do here.'[13] So far he had relied entirely on manual labour.

As a proud postscript, he told the director that George Forrest was collecting for him on the alps of Talifu, and he anticipated some 'good things'. Little did he know that some of those 'good things' would still be cherished in his gardens 90 years on. Forrest found the beautiful *Pieris formosa forrestii* (Plate 4), and its seed was grown at Ness and introduced through Bees. A plant from the original seed now grows as a bush 3.7 m high and 6 m in diameter (see Plate 5). In the early spring the vivid scarlet shoots and the sprays of waxy, white fragrant flowers are a joyous reminder of Forrest's collections for Bulley from that remote part of China.

Further, after crossing the Yangtze river, and climbing to the summit of a pass, at about 4000–4500 m, Forrest found the wonderful blue flowers of *Gentiana sino-ornata* (Plate 20). It was simply called the 'Chinese form' of *Gentiana ornata* for many years. He collected seed when he returned for a second expedition for Bulley in 1910, and it first flowered at Ness and Edinburgh in 1912. Now it is one of his most popular plants, growing easily in moist, acid peaty soil. It has produced some wonderful hybrids, and brings welcome, dazzling colour to any rock garden in the autumn months.

But such successes were the result of great courage, stamina and sturdiness on the part of Forrest. He began with limited knowledge of French or Chinese languages, and lived in fear of hostility from local tribes who were at war with each other and suspicious of 'foreign devils'. Collecting in mountains also meant enormous travail in all conditions of weather. He used his telescope to spot special plants, but it might take great physical exertion to reach them. Moreover, mules could lose their footing on narrow, snowy tracks and he reported that a mule 'fell over a precipice breaking its back in 3 places, and 2 cases which it carried were smashed to atoms'. Precious specimens were lost, coolies had to take on the loads, and with snow up to 5 m deep, it took two days to get over the range.

Through all these difficulties, he was anxious to please Bulley and Balfour. As often as possible, he sent them dried plant specimens and seeds and they arrived in the UK well packed and in good condition. He located flowers whose seeds he would collect later, and he concentrated on herbaceous alpine and sub-alpine species such as gentians and saxifrages, even though the rhododendrons were fascinating him. And he had his pride. When facing the possibility of uprisings, he wrote to Balfour, 'I might as well be scuppered as go home a failure. That is always the logic I have in front of me.'[14]

After months of hardship, he had a fever in early 1905 and the doctor of the Tali mission hospital recommended more rest. Forrest had travelled with the acting British Consul, George Litton, to the high mountains bordering Tibet, and he was already planning to return for the summer:

> Mr Bulley wishes me to go into the Lolo country and if I can get 2 reliable Tibetans to act as guide and servant from the Fathers at Tsekou I will then make the attempt. I should like to work my way right across from Atuntze, that vast tract of country which is blank on all the maps ... and as there have never been Europeans on it before, I think I would be almost certain to get hold of some good new things ... plans ... are subject to Mr Bulley's approval.[15]

Bulley was thrilled to receive letters and seed from Forrest, and to be at the helm of his explorations. He enjoyed the vicarious adventure, and even wrote, 'Don't I jolly well wish I were with them!'[16] He was also genuinely solicitous and sensitive towards Forrest and his fiancée: 'Yunnan is a pretty far away spot, especially when you are in love.' And when he heard that Miss Traill's mother was against the engagement, he supported Forrest by informing Mrs Traill of his high opinion of him, whilst assuring Balfour that he could find work for Miss Traill in Bees' Nursery, if that would help.

Yet Bulley could infuriate Forrest. Small items to Bulley could make a great difference to Forrest, and inconsistencies were maddening. For example, Bulley had insisted that Forrest should take cumbersome photographic equipment with him, and then somehow did not provide the promised printing paper or developing material. When Forrest wrote to request more supplies, 'Mr Bulley ... said there was no necessity to take photos. This after giving me special injunctions to take a camera with me. He is rather a peculiar individual.'[17]

Problems were showing; irritations which were later to split them. For example, while Forrest was staying with a French missionary, Père Monbeig, Monbeig demanded £50 from Bulley for some seeds and herbarium specimens. This seemed exorbitant to Forrest, who was paid £50 a month, and considered that his own collections were also superior. When asked by Bulley to stay on in Yunnan for a third year, Forrest wrote to Balfour, 'I do not think I shall consent, at least not at the present rate of payment ... I like the work I am engaged on ... I should like nothing better than to work under a really good man ...' But Forrest stayed that extra year, and he continued to take photographs. There was a wish to succeed which kept him going.

When he found the famous *Meconopsis integrifolia*, he reported to Balfour, 'I hope to get lots of seed ... I hope Mr Bulley will be pleased with the find ... If I am not the first to send home seed of this species, I hope to be the first to send home photos of it taken *in situ*.'[18]

By this time Bulley's nursery at Ness was firmly established. The catalogue of spring 1905 was a veritable *tour de force*, being more a thick pocket book than a magazine. The list of alpine and herbaceous plants filled 232 pages of small print and no illustrations. Plants were listed alphabetically according to their Latin names, based on the Kew handbook. The choice was amazing: 71 species of *Primula* alone, not including hybrids, varieties or forms.

The majority of plants in the catalogue cost 1s or less. But rare or newly introduced plants were often between 2s 6d and 5s, and Bulley charged 7s 6d for a new monkshood introduced by Wilson, *Aconitum wilsonii* (syn *A. carmichael var. wilsonii*). His most expensive plants included *Primula reidii* at 42s each, as he claimed that he held the entire stock of that species in Britain at the time. If he was able to sell rare plants at that price, no wonder he was excited at the thought of the possible riches that Forrest might bring home.

Indeed, in the summer of 1905, Bulley was in excited mood as 'piles of Forrest's seeds, and also of Père Monbeig's seeds, have germinated already.' He was also having big ideas. King Cotton was flourishing, Liverpool cotton brokers were planning a new, handsome Cotton Exchange, and Bulley planned to expand his nursery business! In July 1905 he was off for a month's exploring tour in the Cork–Waterford district of Ireland, and on to Caen and Dunkirk in France. Eventually he bought a bulb farm at Hillegom, Holland, and a farm on the good alluvial soil at Sealand, near Cheshire.

Forrest, however, was facing a terrible ordeal in the upper Mekong valley, where warring Lamas, Buddhist priests from Tibet, were causing havoc. The first that Bulley knew of it, was a letter from Balfour on 17 August 1905:

The palatial Liverpool Cotton Exchange, opened 2 January 1907, when the imports of cotton into Liverpool reached over 4.25 million bales.

Dear Mr Bulley

You will doubtless have heard through the Foreign Office from Mr Litton that there is little doubt that Forrest has been murdered.

His last letter to me written at Tsekou on 27th May told of the troubles around him – of the murder of French Missionaries and the scarcity of food – but though anxious he seemed to be confident that he would come through all right ...

You will be as we are all here deeply grieved by the catastrophe. He seemed to me to be showing himself a born collector. The dried plants he sent home were in perfect condition, and I gather that you were pleased with the seeds ... I trust that what he has done for you so far may be some recompense to you for your enterprise in sending him out.

Miss Traill to whom I had to break the news this morning is naturally much upset and has gone to his people to tell them ...

Yours very truly
Isaac Bayley Balfour[19]

Bulley was devastated. He replied by return of post:

> Dear Dr Balfour
>
> Your letter has just arrived. I feel very sick. I had no word from the Foreign Office.
>
> The vile feeling is that this fine young fellow was working for pay for me; that he had to do it because he was poor; and that he lost his life in the endeavour to earn my beastly money.
>
> I had frequently told him that safety must be his first consideration and not flowers. And as soon as I got his last letter, I wrote again urging him to run no risks. Of course it never reached him.
>
> I cherish no hope of his being alive. He was too full of pluck …
>
> Sincerely yours
> Arthur K Bulley[20]

He sent Forrest's last letter to Miss Traill and the Forrest family. Fortunately, 36 hours after the first telegram, Balfour received a second, stating that 'Forrest is alive and safe'. He had made a miraculous escape.

A missionary at the China Inland Mission at Talifu wrote that Forrest was on his way to them, and that they would look after him. Specimens of a few new plant species were also salvaged, including the creeping rhododendron, *R. forrestii* (Plate 2) which had been discovered on mossy rocks on the watershed of the Mekong and Salween rivers. When it was first grown in Britain it was hailed as a striking alpine novelty, and it is still admired in gardens today. But searching for it nearly cost Forrest his life.

Balfour tried to console Bulley and to relieve him from his gloom:

> Whatever may happen to Forrest I think you should not lose sight of this aspect of his work – that it is exploration contributing to scientific knowledge and that the life he is leading is that which he longed for, he revels in it, and we could not have realised his wish for it but for your enterprising kindness in employing him.'[21]

But to Bulley, Forrest's experience was a nightmare. He received a brief account from a missionary, W J Embery, at Talifu:

> He escaped after a fearful struggle and experience lasting 21 days, being hunted like a mad dog for 9 days on the hills, suffering terrible privations – then fell in with some friendly people who brought him on his way for quite a distance. Two of the French priests were massacred. F.[Forrest] lost everything he had … [22]

Later it emerged that his French host was brutally tortured to death, and 16 of his 17 collectors and servants died.

Bulley was horrified. When Balfour sent him a sample herbarium label with the title, 'Collected by G Forrest: collector for A K Bulley of Ness, Neston, Cheshire,' Bulley replied, 'You are welcome to use my name on your labels if it is any help to you. Personally I consider the commemoration of money undesirable. Forrest alone is entitled to laurels … '[23]

A dried specimen of Primula bulleyana, collected, named and the notes written by George Forrest, 'collector for A K Bulley'.

Fortunately Forrest bounced back. By September he was planning a journey with Litton to the unexplored upper Salween river valley. Litton was in charge, and he was an experienced and enterprising traveller. So these two tough and energetic men undertook a three-month adventure together, in country which they found to be inhospitable, unhealthy, barbarous but unforgettably beautiful. They met Lissoo men holding huge crossbows with poisoned arrows which could kill a horse, and their journey was made extra difficult by unprecedented flooding, quagmires, landslips and broken bridges. They had to trade for food, but refused a request to barter their breeches for a bag of rice!

They climbed where European feet had never been before, and took in panoramic views of all the great, snow-covered ranges of north-western Yunnan east of the Mekong, from Talifu to the borders of Tibet. In the distance was the glittering 'snow mountain' of Lichiang, and Forrest returned to that range the following year, discovering delights like *Gentiana georgei* and *Primula bulleyana* (Plate 11) in the open mountain meadows, and *P. forrestii* on dry limestone cliffs. There was to be a feast of famous plants for Bees.

However, Litton died of blackwater fever on their return from the Salween valley. So, when Forrest found an unusual and beautiful primula in an alpine pasture on the Lichiang range, he photographed it, collected seed and named it *Primula littoniana* in honour of his friend. Unfortunately, its name had to be changed, when it was realised that it had been previously named *P. vialii* by Delavay. It is a favourite flower today, its glowing red spikes gracing gardens in the summer months (see Plate 9).

After the successful 1906 season it was time for Forrest to return home and be wed, and for the unknown plants to be identified and introduced. Bulley promised he would never let Forrest 'sink into the ranks of the out of works', but Forrest returned to the herbarium in Edinburgh to help sort and name his spoils.

Anticipating good results, Bulley confided, 'I should like to have a collector out somewhere every year!'[24] His money no longer had a 'beastly' feeling. 'Collecting is an expensive joy. But I am afraid I have got it in the blood. Is Bhutan available now? I should like to have a man there.'[25]

Sailing to immortality

Forrest's seeds were germinated in the midst of a thriving concern. Bees Ltd was diversifying and expanding. There was an air of confidence. Crates of bulbs were arriving from the Dutch farm at Hillegom, whilst the Sealand Nursery was producing bulbs and bedding plants, trees, shrubs, roses and herbaceous plants.

Bees' expansion into Holland (1907): at Hillegom, crates of bulbs were loaded on barges to Rotterdam, and grown at Sealand, near Chester.

Penny packets of seeds were produced for the poorer classes who had flower pots or window boxes but little or no land. 'Why buy seeds in 3d packets when a penny packet will satisfy your needs?' The firm moved into larger premises in Liverpool, boasting electric equipment, lights and lifts and a printing plant for 'our own registered design of seed packets'. The seeds were 'cleaned and filled into packets by delicate machinery' and women were employed, which was still rare, outside domestic service.

Catalogues were more inviting, illustrated with flower drawings and light-hearted cartoons, and plant names were given in English as well as Latin. There was now a sundries department, with advertisements ranged from slug traps and fumigators to wooden-soled garden boots lined with thick felt, and 'The largest Shilling Gardening Book ever published'.

Bees Ltd also owned two florist shops on Merseyside, one in Bold Street, Liverpool, and the other in Rock Ferry. To supply the needs of Edwardian elegance, they sold indiarubber flower holders for button holes and produced gents' coat flowers and ladies' shoulder and dress sprays for outings to the opera.

In the spring of 1909 came the new cutting edge in a competitive market. A whole page of its catalogue was devoted to 'New Plants from China'. And with some stretching of the truth, fit to make Forrest fume, the introduction read:

> During the past five years or so we have spent large sums of money in sending collectors out to China. We have now an enormous stock of new plants on trial in our nursery. These we shall exhibit and offer for sale, as they prove of merit ...[26]

Primula malacoides was an early winner. It had been exhibited twice in London and received an award each time. Its name was splashed across the page of the catalogue in large bold letters, and underneath were inserted complimentary quotations from the *Gardeners' Chronicle*, including on 13 March 1909:

> Messrs Bees Ltd, Mill Street, Liverpool, showed a batch of their new *Primula malacoides*. The plants were extremely floriferous, some of them in 4 inch pots having 20 or more inflorescences. The plant is a splendid acquisition amongst greenhouse subjects for winter blooming.

What a great beginning for Forrest's flowers! Bees charged 7s 6d per plant;

68s a dozen. It was an arable weed in Yunnan, but it has been an enormous success for greenhouse or conservatory culture here, plant selection producing many spectacular strains. In the 1950s it was reckoned to be Forrest's most important introduction, and the entire European stock was probably derived from Forrest's first sending of seeds to Bees.

Vying in importance is the primula which Forrest named *Primula bulleyana* (Plate 11) in honour of his patron. It came from mountain meadows at an altitude of 3000–3500 m, on the Lichiang range, and received immediate acclaim when shown at the Horticultural Hall, Westminster. Messrs Bees' stall was tucked away in an annexe, but this plant's beauty shone out and was awarded one of only two first-class certificates in the show (the other was for a rhododendron shown by Veitch). Glowing press reports followed: the *Gardeners' Chronicle* had three illustrations of *P. bulleyana* in one issue.

That was good selling power, and Bees' catalogue enthused on the tiers of whorled flowers in glorious colours:'buff, orange, apricot, and scarlet all enter into it.' Strong plants were sold for 5s each. It was first grown in a damp wood at Ness, and in the Royal Botanic Garden, Edinburgh. Ever since then, drifts of it have become a popular feature of many gardens and garden calendars.

How pleased Bulley would be to know this! He had refused to allow his name to be attached to one 'beastly … saxifrage', saying 'I won't sail into immortality on that,'[27] but he must have been delighted to do so with *P. bulleyana*. He felt so personally associated with it that during a retirement trip to New Zealand he introduced himself by saying, 'I am *Primula bulleyana*.'

So 1909 started triumphantly for Bulley. Three of Forrest's primulas were awarded first-class certificates: *P. bulleyana*, *P. forrestii* and *P. littoniana* (now *P. vialii*) (Plate 9) and *P. malacoides* was given an award of merit. Moreover, Kew purchased plants of all these from Bees. Bulley felt good. The nightmare of Forrest's near death was turning into the radiant reality of beautiful new flowers. People were coming from afar to see them. The American, David Fairchild, who was in charge of Plant Introduction for the US Government, made a visit to Ness in August 1909. He described it as 'one of the largest collections of Chinese ornamental plants in Great Britain.'[28]

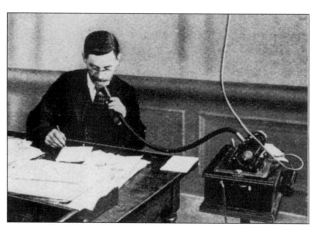

Bees' catalogues, 1910–12, boasted new Liverpool offices with modern electric machinery. This dictaphone recorded sound by a stylus on a wax cylinder.

The typists heard the message in their ear phones from a transcribing machine powered by a foot pedal.

But Bulley got carried away in his charges. As a Fabian he was introducing new flowers for everyone's benefit, but as a businessman he wanted a profit! On 4 May 1909 he reported that he had sold about 20 *Primula forrestii* at 10s 6d. 'I was surprised to find that the masses of very rich people who admired the plant at the RHS stuck at the price. Kudos remains ... Well, luckily the commercial isn't the only side of these ventures.'[29] He charged half that price for a strong plant in the next catalogue.

Commercial necessities now drove Bulley hard and he decided that plants of value should have:

> the purely advertising, commercial name of Bees [see Plates 14–17]. I am sure that from the commercial point of view we have made a great mistake in not using it before. I grow green when I think what the advertising value of *Ampelopsis veitchii* has probably been ... Beesii is nice and crisp, though it breaks all rules of declension ... However I am indifferent. Beesi, Beesorum, Beesensis, Beesium, Beesica, Beesiana, anything which brings the name in ...[30]

But when Kew named a Chinese gentian *Gentiana veitchiorum*, Bulley thought it sounded hideous, and that tipped *Beesiana* into favour. In 1913 Bulley was still pushing for it, even when herbarium specimens were being sent to Germany for identification:

> I must make it a definite condition, that good things are to be called *Beesiana. Bulleyana* may come second. Will you please pass this on in such a way that there will be no mistake about it. Hardly anything has got Bees' name in the Marburg determinations, and I see Veitch gets his name on everything.[31]

Rhododendron beesianum (Plate 17) results from this plea, and in the end there were 12 species named after Bees, including some still grown today, such as *Allium beesianum* (Plate 16) and *Jasminum beesianum* (Plate 15). Twenty-two species were named after Bulley from Forrest's first expedition to north-west Yunnan in China, including *Androsace bulleyana*, *Diapensia bulleyana* and *Delphinium bulleyanum*.

The legacy left is also that plants named *bulleyana(um)* and *beesiana(um)* are growing on the mountains of Yunnan. A Liverpool cotton broker's enterprise in plant collection and his thrust for economic success in Britain, are reflected in the names of Chinese plants on Chinese mountains.

Primula beesiana, photographed by George Forrest in Yunnan, and used by Bees Ltd in their 1912 catalogue. At the time, photography made purplish petals appear white.

Dissension and praise

Forrest was restless to return to Yunnan. It was as if he had staked out his territory on a rich seam and he wanted to return for more valuable pickings. But early in 1909 Bulley was reluctant to commit himself. 'There is nothing in the world I should like more than to send Forrest out next autumn. If I possibly can I will. But the simple facts are that I can't see it costing less than £600 a year, and that I am a comparatively poor man.'[32] (Bees Ltd had only recently moved its premises within Liverpool.) Bulley would reconsider in the autumn; Forrest had to wait.

An American, Charles Sprague Sargent, had asked Forrest to collect for him in northern China, but Forrest was not interested. In desperation, Sargent even asked Bulley if he could persuade Forrest to change his mind, but to no avail. Fairchild also put out feelers to Forrest. But then the summer successes of Forrest's first Chinese plants imbued Bulley with new confidence. He offered to pay Forrest to return to his favourite area, the Lichiang range, Yunnan. There would be a salary of £200 per annum, plus expenses of over £600. He would pay Forrest for 15 months from 11 December 1909. The total outlay for Bees Ltd would be £933 9s 4d.[33] Forrest had hoped for a salary of £300, as he now had a wife and child to support. But he was in no position to bargain. He was being offered the opportunity he had yearned for, and there was a possibility of the contract being extended for two more years. He sailed from Liverpool in January 1910 on his second expedition for Bees Ltd. Meanwhile, to defray the costs, Bulley did a deal with a keen rhododendron enthusiast, J C Williams. If he would pay £300 to Bees Ltd, he could have all the seeds of rhododendrons and conifers. And Bulley looked forward to the rest of the loot.

While Forrest was on his way, the extraordinary richness of the Chinese flora was unfolding before Bulley's eyes. When two new-looking irises opened into flower, he sent them to the expert, W R Dykes, a school master at Charterhouse, who named them *Iris forrestii* and *I. bulleyana*. Soon there was a full-page article on them in the *Gardeners' Chronicle*,[34] in which Bulley had the satisfaction of seeing these two irises alongside one of Veitch's. His dreams were coming true! As if to verify his perfect timing, a Hardy Plant Society began that summer, for 'the encouragement, the extension and the improvement of hardy plant culture'.

Incarvillea mairei advertised by Bees Ltd, 1913. George Forrest collected seed and it has been in cultivation ever since.

3959. Bees' Crimson Trumpet Flower.
A glorious mass of colour in May. Tuberous-rooted and quite hardy. One of the finest plants sent home by our collector from the Chinese Alps.

His flare for publicity was also canny. He now had five florist shops in Liverpool, so he showed cut flowers at the shows of the Liverpool Horticultural Society, and claimed a silver medal in July 1910. In the same month, Bees showed their new primulas at the RHS Summer Exhibition at Holland House, after doing the same in York. Bees now had a picture of *P. forrestii* on headed notepaper and boasted about its collector in catalogues. A reporter from *The Gentleman's Journal and Gentlewoman's Court Review* wrote a detailed and complimentary account of the firm and its up-to-date new premises, and this was made into a booklet for distribution.

But all was not well with Forrest. This was the expedition he had yearned for, but on arrival in Rangoon he was devastated to learn that he had been let down. Bees Ltd had sent him insufficient money. He could not buy all he needed for the expedition. A cablegram to Bees elicited £150, but the damage was done: Forrest was angry and disillusioned. Already homesick, missing his wife and child, feeling lonely and depressed, this was the last straw. There had been a mix-up at Bees' office. Moreover, delays in payment recurred. Bulley 'regretted' this, admitting 'to have a man in the remoteness of China short of funds is shocking.'[35] Why didn't he supervise more carefully? His enthusiasms were not always matched by his management skills; he did not always delegate successfully. Certainly it was ironic that whilst Bulley was 'taking up the Workers' battle' in a Rossendale election, his plant hunter was left in the lurch. Moreover, Bulley did not realise that a word of praise or appreciation of Forrest's work would have been like gold to him. Everything got on top of Forrest and he threatened to resign. But Bulley called his bluff by writing, 'I shall not want any formal notice of your desire to go.' The storm passed, though Forrest declared 'If ever I go anywhere again as a collector, it shall never be for Messrs Bees Ltd.'[36] Indeed, he did not want to be harnessed to the commercial interests of any nurseryman. Bitterness towards them had set in. He maintained that Bulley was 'a cad of the first order', explaining 'there is a lot said about the meaness of the Scotch but in my time I have met more stingy English than ever I did Scotch, and Bulley and Veitch, the great Sir Harry, are types, extreme types!'[37]

However, Forrest drank in the beauty of his surroundings, and he was soon hard at work for Bulley. Despite incessant rain and other troubles, he did his best to obtain a good harvest. He found *Roscoea humeana* (Plate 19), introduced *Gentiana sino-ornata* (Plate 20), and learned more about the distribution of many plants. In turn, Bulley offered Forrest the opportunity to continue for two more years. However, Forrest was keen to return to his family, and his preferences now lay with rhododendrons. It was time for the two men to move in different directions. Forrest transferred to the sponsorship of J C Williams, under whom he even had a bonus for each new rhododendron species! And before Forrest's second expedition had ended Bulley wrote to Balfour, 'I expect that by Jan. 1912 I shall be thirsting to send someone out again. Have you the right person?'[38]

Forrest returned to Yunnan for five more expeditions, and he and Bulley kept in contact, especially if Bulley wanted something! And after the First World War, when Forrest was dependent on the sponsorship of syndicates of gardeners, Bulley immediately bought shares in return for seeds.

Meanwhile, Bulley's enterprise, in being the first to send Forrest to Yunnan, was not forgotten by the scientists who were to work on Forrest's specimens for years to come. A single epiphytic orchid, spurred on its central lip, prompted one of the finest tributes that taxonomists could offer. Forrest found the orchid growing on trunks of trees in moist forests on the Tali range in 1906, at about 2500–2750 m altitude. It was sent to Berlin for identification by an orchid expert, Rudolph Schlechter, who found it to be so different from any other orchid in the world, that he put it in a new genus, *Bulleyia*. The orchid was named *Bulleyia yunnanensis* (Plate 18), and in his dedication of the new genus, Schlechter wrote:

> It gives me great satisfaction to be able to dedicate this genus to Mr A K Bulley, who, by sending out such an able collector as Mr G Forrest, has greatly advanced our knowledge of the Flora of the more unknown parts of China.[39]

5

Kingdon Ward:
The Search Widens

To every man — even to a plant collector — a dream is given
(KINGDON WARD, 1924)[1]

Bulley loved chess, and his widening search for more alpines was like a great game of chess, the world being his chess board. High mountain areas were like squares to be aimed for and captured for their booty. His collectors were the pawns to be moved according to the state of the game. Moves had to be planned ahead, and some strategies kept in reserve. It was fun and challenging, but he needed the men to move around the board. Who would be next?

'Bulley's letter decided my life'

Sometimes Bulley seemed to have all the luck, and finding Ward was extraordinary. It was December 1910. Bulley consulted Professor Balfour who replied, 'There is a very good man in China now.'[2] This was Frank Kingdon Ward, the son of an old friend of Balfour. He was 26 years old, a school master in Shanghai, and itching to go on an expedition. He had a Cambridge Tripos in Natural Sciences and a 'good knowledge of botany and of plants'. Balfour liked the lad, thought he was better fitted for the work than Forrest was when Bulley first took him on, and that Ward was unlikely to become conceited if successful. Bulley didn't waste even a day; he telegraphed Balfour: 'Please post Ward's address.'[3]

Bulley's overture to Ward was most timely. Ward had already travelled by junk and on foot across the breadth of China, collecting birds and animals on an American zoological expedition financed by the Duke of Bedford. He had loved exploring wild, unspoiled country and now the classroom hemmed him in, but he had no money to do otherwise. His widowed mother tried to help by writing

Francis Kingdon Ward
(1885–1958)

to a family friend, Oldfield Thomas, who was Keeper of Zoology at the Natural History Museum in London. Thanks to him, Ward had been invited on the Bedford expedition, so Mrs Ward pleaded, 'If an opportunity occurs of similar work may I ask you to remember him? Expeditions I know are not very frequent but I believe he would be an acquisition to any, his heart is so set on the work ...' [4] Meanwhile, Ward had to try and settle in the school classroom, a reluctant teacher nursing an ambition to return to the snow-capped mountains of western China, a youngster inspired and ripe for adventure. He later explained, 'Travel had bitten too deeply into my soul.' [5]

> ... and then suddenly, out of the blue, came a ... letter from a stranger, asking me if I would like to go on a one-man expedition; this time it was to be plant-hunting! The letter was from Arthur K. Bulley... [6]

Bulley's offer arrived in January 1911 and Ward accepted at once. This was a dream come true! He broke his contract and left Shanghai a month later to begin his plant-hunting career. He was off to collect hardy and alpine plants from the mountains of Yunnan and the wild Tibetan marches. Bulley's letter had been a turning point in his life. He later recollected, 'Bulley's letter decided my life ... for the next forty-five years.' [7]

However, Ward's path to success as a plant hunter had many ups and downs, and taxed Bulley's patience to its limits. By instinct Ward was an explorer, and sometimes his plant hunting seemed to come second. He was in his element in unknown territory: a *Boy's Own* character with a touch of daring, following an impulse even if it led him into trouble. At first he was not as well-equipped for plant hunting as he had imagined. His academic education gave him no knowledge of garden plants, and he was rejected by the American, David Fairchild, when he was looking for a trained 'field man' to collect Chinese economic plants. But this is where Bulley's opportunism was a boon. He would take the risk. There was a keen young man 'on the spot' with good academic credentials and some experience: Bulley took the chance gladly. Ward was keen to prove himself, and Bulley had to be understanding of Ward's lowly position on the 'learning curve' of a plant hunter.

Bulley's decision was to be fully justified. He and Ward swapped sponsorship and seeds for more than 20 years and Ward was to introduce some wonderful garden plants. Ward's successes led to him receiving the Victoria Medal of Honour in Horticulture, the highest honour the RHS can bestow, and volume 162 (1940) of *Curtis's Botanical Magazine* was dedicated to Ward two years before Bulley died.

Right from the beginning there was evidence that Ward had an eye for a valuable plant. Whilst on his zoological expedition in China, he had collected a new Chinese species, *Jasminum wardii*. However, there was an amazing coincidence, for it was later considered synonymous with *Jasminum beesianum* (Plate 15), previously collected by George Forrest. [8] Forrest had introduced this beautiful, fragrant shrub into Britain through Bees Ltd, and it is widely available today. Even before Ward's official plant hunting had begun, this innocent flower provided a unique link between Forrest, Ward and Bees Ltd,

Liverpool. The game of chess could continue. Ward was to hunt for new herbaceous plants in the mountains of Yunnan, but avoiding Forrest's main stamping ground. It was up to Ward to prove himself. Bulley had put faith in him, and Ward left school teaching in Shanghai without looking back.

Ward's adventures and Bulley's fears

Once in Yunnan, Ward set off from Tengyueh in March 1911, on the main pack road. On the advice of Litton's successor, acting Consul Rose, he was heading for Atuntze, a little village in the far north-west of Yunnan, nestling in a horseshoe of mountains east of the Mekong river at 3350 m. It was off the line of posts and telegraphs, but there were numerous Chinese merchants and a garrison of a hundred men, which could be useful in those unsettled days near the Tibetan border. This was to be his base for six months, from the first flowers opening to the time for collecting seeds. Forrest had not explored this far north, so Ward had a good chance of success in finding plants new to science and horticulture. There was a joyous note of spring in the air, high hopes in his heart, and a great sense of adventure. It was his great opportunity, and Bees flew the flag by proudly announcing in its catalogue that a new collector was now working in remote regions with the promise of good things to come.

Later in the year, the 1912 Bees' catalogue had to be written, and the public hunger for new and rare plants was fed with more details:

> Mr F. Kingdon Ward is working the Mekong–Salween divide. The Mekong and Salween rivers … cut through vast mountain ranges of immense altitude. It is on the slopes of these snow-capped giants that untold riches of the Chinese Flora flourish unseen and almost unsuspected. We are convinced, from the reports of our collectors [Forrest and Ward], that the plants so far brought to light are but a 'drop in the well'. So trying is the climate, and so risky the intercourse with natives, that only a mere patch of ground has been covered after several years' strenuous work and the expenditure of considerable sums of money.

An extract from one of Ward's letters was included in the catalogue. It listed differently coloured flowers of *Meconopsis* and *Primula*, saxifrages and paeonies and others from which he had collected seed, and others that he hoped for. It emphasised the great effort that Ward was making to procure a range of first-class seed, even risking his own life among the wildlife: 'A few days ago I was in the forest enveloped in clouds of rain, when a big black bear stood up 10 yards from me!'[9]

However, for a whole year Bulley had a rather fearful, frustrating wait. Six months after Ward left Shanghai, Bulley admitted, 'I had a line (literally) from Ward posted at Tengyueh. Since that nothing. I haven't a notion where he is going.'[10] Poor Bulley! There were an awful lot of unknowns. When a year had passed, Bulley even feared for Ward's judgement of a good plant, when his apparent 'best loot' was from the family Scrophulariaceae, which 'Forrest hardly touched'. The last straw was the news that Ward was taking an unknown route on his return to Tengyueh. Then Bulley voiced a fear which was to haunt him many times in his dealings with Ward: 'I think he is more a geographer than a botanist (though I may be wrong on this), and that travel *per se* is always very desirable to him. I doubt if he would care for Forrest's fixed camp, or not more than 2 bases, through the season.'[11]

Balfour painted a more hopeful picture: Ward wrote enthusiastically about his work, was a keen botanist, and now had some knowledge of the flora of Yunnan. If Bulley were to give him another chance, and explain the sort of things that would be useful to him, Balfour would help Ward botanically. It would be worthwhile, because 'There are a number of beautiful things not yet in cultivation which must be quite common in Yunnan.'[12]

With these assurances, Bulley bucked up. He genuinely liked Ward and looked forward to him staying a whole weekend at Ness. At least he would hear first-hand news of the expedition. Ward was already writing a book about his adventures, *The Land of the Blue Poppy*, and from this we can feel the freshness of his story, the range of his exploits, and the thrill of the hunt.[13]

One summer morning he had climbed above the tree line on the mountains overlooking Atuntze. 'Looking across the rugged slope, I saw at a little distance a flash of shining azure blue.' Could it be a blue stone, he wondered, but what stone could be such a heavenly blue? His eyes scanned the scree around him. Had he made a real discovery of the first importance? Then, in a crevice nearby 'was the most bewitching blue flower I had ever seen – several blooms on a long raceme! So, incredibly, it was a flower, the first blue poppy I had ever encountered.'[14] He wrote a long description of it to Bulley and sent it by runner (a 10-day trip) to the nearest post office. Bulley discussed it with Forrest, and eventually it was decided that the poppy must be *Meconopsis speciosa*, found previously by Forrest, but not yet growing in any garden in Britain. In the late autumn Ward returned up that mountain to collect plenty of seed.

It needed a tough, fit and athletic person to travel and survive in those remote mountains. Fortunately, also, Ward had an innate love of plunging into anything which offered a degree of novelty. He showed this in his resourceful approach to finding food. He drank yak milk and could make a meal of sorrel and young leaves. He ate whole rhododendron flowers for the nourishment of the 'big drop of honey' at the base of the corolla. For meat he had raw finch and fried voles (*Microtus wardii*). On one occasion he stripped off his clothes and swam through the snow-melt waters of the Yangtze river, to collect a Brahmin duck which he'd shot for his next meal. Another time, he swapped two cakes of Vinolia soap for a haunch of bacon, a chicken and some eggs!

Ward loved camping under the stars by a river, lulled to sleep by the roar of the torrent. 'A thundering torrent was music to me, and lying in bed I would watch the brilliant arc of the new moon set over the mountains.' He was sensitive to the charm of a sunset and the perfume of *Asclepias* in full bloom. He listened to the sounds of cicadas chirping, bullfrogs groaning and the drums beating as a prayer for rain. Yet he put up with sleeping in a crowded room while the 'odour and grunts of sundry pigs rose up between the loose floor boards.'

He tolerated the tedium of waiting for unavailable mules and missing baggage, and the loneliness of receiving no mail for weeks on end. He knew feelings of utter desolation and 'paralysing isolation'. Threats of civil war vied with mountain robbers to upset his plans. There was friction between the Chinese and Tibetans, the English were often hated 'foreigners', and rumours were rife as the Manchu dynasty crumbled into chaos.

One summer afternoon at 5 p.m. Ward received an alarming message: 'The English are in Lhasa … The Chinese … swear to exterminate every Englishman. I fear you will be killed before the end. You must leave Atuntse at once.' By 8 a.m. the next morning he was on the road north to Batang, with one pony, three porters and a solitary soldier as escort – and a heavy Colt automatic pistol in his pocket. It was a record-breaking 'flight' covering 180 mountainous miles in six days instead of the usual eight. When they arrived, they found it was only a rumour. Relieved, Ward typically took advantage of being there to make one of his unauthorised, thrilling, exploratory detours into Tibet.

He recorded everything as he went along, from details of dress and tribal customs to wide-ranging scientific observations. He studied geological outcrops and plant ecology, he thought about plant distributions and past glaciation. Changes of climate were recorded as automatically as changes of landscape. His feeling for geography was as keen as Bulley surmised. He was thrilled at first seeing the great Yangtze river, 2500 miles from its mouth. When he crossed a high mountain pass which was clear of snow for only 2–3 months a year, he felt exhilaration in his location: 'Behind us lay China, in front Tibet.' He was one of only a few European explorers who had ever reached these Tibet–China borderlands.

But what about his seeds? Those tiny treasures he had been paid to collect? Ward could look back and claim that 'Never had I enjoyed myself more,' but was he successful in the main aim of the expedition for Bees of Liverpool?

The packets of seeds were emptied from his bag on to the grand piano in Bulley's sitting room at Ness in early March 1912. There were 76 different packets. This was less than half the number of plants which he recorded. And some of the seed was in minuscule amounts. Bulley was mighty glad to see them, but probably thought that there were not as many as Forrest would have collected! However, he was thankful that Ward was back safely, and sympathetic to Ward's story of the problems which he had encountered.

It was often a problem of timing and inexperience in a new country and new flora. Sometimes he simply missed the vital time for seed ripening, or did not return to the marked place in the autumn, did not find the plants elsewhere or did not recognise the plant in its autumnal dress. Late rains were a handicap to seed collection, and there was only Ward and his servant to do all the chores: picking, packing, numbering and drying the seed. When it poured with rain, the seed had to be dried by a charcoal burner in his room. It was laborious, and time was against him, for some flowers which were marked carefully in the summer were covered in deep snow by the time he returned to them. Some were successfully dug out, but others could not be found.

To reduce risks, the seed was shared with Balfour. Bulley enclosed a letter with the precious packets: 'You do better with many of these things than we do, and none of these irreplaceable rarities ought if it can be avoided to be lost. I know I can rely on your keeping everything in the Gardens till Bees have distributed. Hope you have luck, especially with *Meconopsis speciosa*.'[15]

In April 1912 the *Titanic* collided with an iceberg and sank to the ocean bed. It was an ill-fated maiden voyage, and Bulley had analogous fears that Ward's 'maiden' expedition for him might end in disaster, with seeds and plants lost to cultivation. After only about six weeks his nervousness showed in a letter to Balfour: 'Germination so far has been very poor … my impression is that the germination of Forrest's seeds was far better. I wonder whether there has been anything lacking in ripeness, drying or packing? … Have you sown in cold frames or under heat?'[16] 'Don't panic', was the gist of Balfour's reply, couched in more courteous terms.

Meanwhile, Bulley had other things on his mind. Bees was to exhibit at the Royal International Horticultural Exhibition which the King opened at Chelsea on 22 May 1912. Comparisons were being made with the Exhibition of 1866, when Bulley was only five years old. The number of classes had nearly doubled, and rock and water gardens were not seen in 1866. Now they were an expanding part of the horticultural scene. Rock gardens, complete with moraines and screes, were becoming fashionable and needed plants! This is where Bulley was trying to find a niche, as part of another quiet revolution: 'This realm, this England' of 1912 was exhibiting new plants not only from its own Empire, but from the far 'Celestial Empire'. And not from the gardens or coast of China, but from the remote, unexplored mountains.

Everyone who was anyone in the world of horticulture would be there, from friends like Dr A Henry and Correvon to members of the Veitch family and representatives of Kew. Socialist Bulley was not interested in the grand banquet, but in commerce. It was a grand opportunity to show off the value of George Forrest's plants, and Bees romped away with six medals and a Diploma of Honour. Then in June Bees was awarded the Farrer Cup for six new and rare dwarf rock garden plants. They were heady days for Bees' success with new Chinese plants.[17] What a spur to more plant collecting! The suffragettes were singing 'March! March!' but Bulley's electioneering days were nearly over and he was marching to his equally determined goal of plant introduction.

However, should it be with Ward? He must decide by the autumn. During a month's holiday in the Breganzer Wald, hiring a horse and carriage to climb the passes, and delighting in colonies of the slipper orchard, *Cypripedium calceolus*, Bulley pondered this question. Ward wanted to return, and Balfour backed him, thinking he would develop and learn. Bulley admired Ward's many qualities but still had nagging doubts. He did not want to risk an expedition with dubious gains. Most importantly, would Ward put all his efforts into plant collection? He was writing numerous articles and a book about his travels, and maybe journalism would suit him best? Bulley decided he would write to Ward, 'urging him, if he felt he could do better things, to leave plant and seed collecting to a man without journalistic gifts.'[18]

Then Balfour sent news that Ward's herbarium specimens included three primulas new to science! These were *Primula wardii*, *P. atuntsiensis* and *P. vernicosa*. The first of these were later found to be the same as *P. yargongensis*, but still there were five new species of saxifrage, and two new species of gentian, *Gentiana wardii* and *G. atuntsiensis*. Altogether 22 new species were announced within a year of Ward's return,[19] including a new meconopsis, *M. wardii* (although now regarded as a variety of *M. henrici*). So Ward had made an undoubted contribution to science.

Sadly, most of Ward's new species proved of little gardening significance, except *Androsace wardii*, a neat and desirable rock garden plant. Some re-introductions were useful and exciting, as when Bulley thought 'Ward's "scarlet Primula" is going to be *Androsace bulleyana*, one of the very finest of Forrest's things, of which I have never succeeded in working up any stock.'[20] As for *Meconopsis speciosa*, it was like the big fish that always got away. By sending two collectors to different areas of north-west Yunnan, Bulley twice tapped this beautiful plant of very limited distribution in China. That was an achievement in itself; only his own collectors had ever found it. But growing it was difficult. After apparent germination success, Bulley triumphantly sent plants to Kew and Edinburgh in August 1912, only to find that there had been some mistake in the numbering of the packets, and that these plants were really *Meconopsis wardii*. What a disappointment! Forrest and Ward both collected seed of *M. speciosa* in later years, but if the seed germinated, the seedlings were always lost in the second year. It is tantalisingly beautiful on the Yunnan mountains, but will not grow well in our gardens.[21] *C'est la vie!* The trials and tribulations of trying to introduce new garden plants to Britain: Bulley and his collectors knew them all.

Ward admitted that this first expedition for Bulley was 'a poor start' and 'not a rousing success' but he was sure that he could do better, and that his journalism would not interfere with his prime task of plant and seed collection. After all, writing in an evening replaced company on a solo expedition. Finally, it was agreed that he would work for Bulley for two more years.[22] Ward revisited Edinburgh for more discussion of techniques and a pile of the latest publications on newly discovered species. He was equipped and ready.

High hopes and drama

Whither to send Ward? Would China's political turmoil make it too risky? Would its borders even be open? Sun Yat-sen and his nationalist movement had succeeded in driving out the Manchu dynasty, replacing it by a republic, but there was civil war and great confusion in China. Thoughts buzzed round in Bulley's head as he considered alternative areas for Ward to explore. One suggestion was the Indian state of Manipur and entering Tibet from there. But when Bulley consulted the *Encyclopaedia Britannica*, he was not impressed by the fact that the highest altitude seemed to be 8000 feet (2400 m). Bulley's mind ranged from the Andes to any other part of the Himalayas. He asked Balfour's advice and after reading in the *Manchester Guardian* that an expedition was back from the 'Karakoram unknowns' he wrote to ask about the flora. After reading a notice in the *Gardeners' Chronicle* of a book enumerating plants of the high Karakoram, he searched for that. 'If China is closed Ward may have to go there.'[23]

However, it seems that Ward's mind was made up! As early as March of that year, he told the Natural History Museum that he would return to south-east Tibet in 1913 and would collect some small mammals. By November 1912, he was taking a crash course in surveying and map-making, learning field astronomy at the Observatory, Cambridge, and writing to the Royal Geographical Society, asking for the loan of surveying equipment! He explained, 'I propose to go back to the region I was in last year ... to get in to unexplored as well as unsurveyed country' although he admitted that 'there is a good chance of the whole thing failing on account of the distracted state of the country.'[24]

In a letter to Balfour in December 1912, Bulley wrote: 'Ward sails at the end of February. I haven't an idea where he is going. But I feel sure he has made up his mind to do a lot better than last time ... For one thing he will employ 4 collectors instead of one.'[25] Bees was paying him, and there is no hint that Ward was not satisfied with the amount. In the next two years he even saved about £300, with the fee from Bees, prudence, and the small amount he earned from writing.

Bees' 1913 catalogue reads like a cross between a mystery tour, a fairy story and a real-life *Boy's Own* adventure:

> It is a pleasure to assure our clients that our activities in search of new plants show no abatement. Since Mr. Forrest completed his second expedition, Mr. F. Kingdon Ward has returned [January 1912] with a goodly parcel of seeds, and is already on his way out again in quest of further prizes. His destination on this trip must not be avowed ... Whether it is Ward's intention to burrow a way into the interior or follow the flight of the eagles we cannot say. That he will eventually get there we feel sure. That he will 'see things' is past doubt. And that he will return with a full 'bag' and some thrilling tales we have every confidence. Ward and Forrest have, between them, arranged a meeting somewhere – out East – in the early months of 1913. Possibly they are comparing notes even as you read this. Does it not stir one's blood to think of these men calmly plotting to get through the wild passes between two continents, which, to use a newspaper phrase, are simply seething with rebellion and anarchy.[26]

Bees was unashamedly trying to arouse people's interest and catch the mood for daring exploits as the world rang with the story of Captain Scott's dead body being found with those of his colleagues in the frozen wastes of Antarctica. In reality, all was not entirely well between Forrest and Ward. Forrest was wary and scathingly reported that Ward spent two weeks at Lichiang 'playing around with theodolite, plane table, compass and other instruments which he had on loan.' By June, Ward had not started on his plant collecting at Atuntze and his casual approach made Forrest sceptically remark, 'I wonder if he intends collecting at all this season.' With heavy irony and a feeling of superiority, he continued, 'Bulley's well served by him! No wonder he only collected 150 species in 1911.'[27]

But Balfour threw down the gauntlet for both men in April 1913, as Ward entered Yunnan. Balfour gave a lecture on 'Chinese species of Primula' at a Primula Conference and declared that 'only the fringe of the Chinese primulas has been touched.' He pointed out that the Chinese species already discovered probably outnumbered all other known species of *Primula*, and that 'in the near future large numbers of new and valuable species may be expected.'

Now it was for Ward, as well as Forrest, to prove Balfour to be correct, and he made a good start. For, despite Forrest's jibes, he found *Primula chungensis* on approaching the Chungtien plateau, before he reached Atuntze. He introduced this golden-flowered 'candelabra' primula to cultivation together with the popular, beautiful and lemon-yellow flowered *Rhododendron wardii*, which he discovered on the Do-kar-la, a pass on the pilgrims' road round the sacred mountain of Ka-kar-po.

Bulley had installed a new man, Dixon, to grow Ward's seeds commercially. Bees' catalogue now had a coloured cover and Bulley had high hopes of more plants called *Beesiana*. However, *en route* for a summer holiday in the Cottian Alps, Bulley tempered hope with some reserve:

> He is not a born collector like F [Forrest]. But I am sure he is deeply feeling the poverty of his haul last season, and is going to do his best. He wrote me a despondent line just before meeting F. Of course I replied cheering him up as well as I could. But without doubt he is faced with the fading of a golden dream. If he is to do his job well, he has to stop within a limited area and work it well. Charming tours of exploration will have to be given up. It's rather rough on him. We shall have to see how he gets on.[28]

Within three months there was bad news. Bulley reported:

> Ward is very depressed. He has been swindled on his mule contract ... robbed of £20; is disliked by the officials; and is generally in the soup. He invites me to supersede him on account of his evident incompetency. I shan't. The poor chap is cursed by himself – just like Forrest. But he knows it and owns it. F. doesn't.[29]

Balfour agreed but tried to give some good news too, 'There are some very nice things amongst the seeds that

Bees' Sundries Department advertised goods from lawn mowers to natural perfumes 'such as are supplied to Queen Alexandra'.

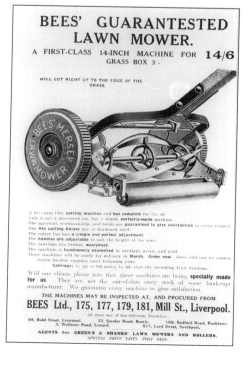

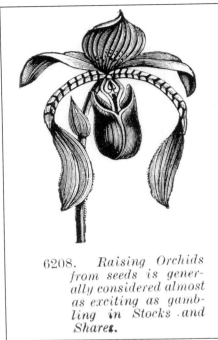

6208.   Raising Orchids from seeds is generally considered almost as exciting as gambling in Stocks and Shares.

An interesting viewpoint from a cotton broker's seed firm!

Ward got. I am pretty sure he has got *Primula blattariformis* ... and certainly his P. *pseudocapitata* is well worth growing.'

Ward tried to retrieve this 1913 expedition in the remaining two months, and conscientiously collected, sorted and packeted seed. In October Bulley received 'the first fruits from Ward' and shared them joyously with Kew and Edinburgh. *Primula bracteata* and P. *henrici* were introduced to cultivation, but the 1913 expedition was not horticulturally very valuable, and there were no more 'beesiana' flowers for sale. His collection of dried plants was better than his first one – nothing like Forrest's in profuseness and variety, but scientifically interesting.

While Bulley sought someone 'cunning with his pen' who could write catalogues and advertisements 'in an interesting way', Ward then added unwanted and disastrous drama. Instead of retiring thankfully to winter quarters for a rest before the 1914 collecting season, he was determined to explore part of Tibet, taking his surveying equipment with him. It was a complete failure. China and Tibet were at war and the Chinese authorities were concerned for his safety. He tried daring ruses to enter Tibet, but he had no passport with him, and he would not listen to the warnings of the people. He played his gramophone to charm the locals, but officialdom would not budge, even with bribes. Ward gave up, but the damage was done. He was banished from exploring or collecting in China and Tibet. As Balfour said, 'He was indiscreetly impulsive and has had to pay the penalty.' So did Bulley! Ward's yearnings for exploration had jeopardised his own plant collecting. Bulley felt depressed and in April 1914 he wrote, 'I don't think that Ward will ever make a collector. I think he had better tack on to something else – perhaps journalism.'[30] This was not the news for Bees' catalogues ... and Bees had promised pay for another year.

However, all was not lost. Ward retreated to upper Burma, under British rule! He collected plants in the Kachin Hills on the Burma–Yunnan border and showed the western extension of many Chinese plants. Bees sent on to Kew 150 packets of Ward's seeds from there. They included new rhododendrons and the successful purple-flowering *Primula burmanica*, which is closely related to P. *bulleyana*, and has proved to be a vigorous, easy-going, garden plant. Faith in Ward was renewed before the First World War swept him into the Indian army. Bulley was quick to sponsor Ward after the First World War, though he was never the sole sponsor again. But, as we shall see, his loyalty was to be rewarded by some superb discoveries in the early 1920s, plants which were to enrich our gardens permanently.

Meanwhile, both Forrest in China and Ward in Burma found new plants which were to immortalise further the name of Bees Ltd. They were not showy, though they were in the buttercup family, Ranunculaceae, and they did not fit

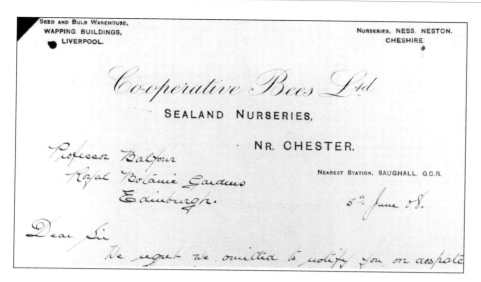

SEED AND BULB WAREHOUSE,
WAPPING BUILDINGS,
LIVERPOOL.

NURSERIES, NESS. NESTON.
CHESHIRE.

Co-operative Bees Ltd

SEALAND NURSERIES,

NR. CHESTER.

NEAREST STATION, SAUGHALL, G.C.R.

Professor Balfour
Royal Botanic Gardens
Edinburgh.

5th June 08.

Dear Sir

We regret we omitted to notify you on despatc

Telephone:- 5020 Royal.
Telegrams:- BEES, Toxteth, Liverpool.

NURSERIES:-
NESS,
NESTON, CHESHIRE.
SEALAND,
Nr. CHESTER.
KILLEGOM,
HOLLAND.

Bees Limited

175-181, MILL ST,
LIVERPOOL.

August 10th. 1911.

The Regius Keeper,
    Botanic Garden,
        Edinburgh.

SHOPS
98, BOLD ST, LIVERPOOL, 21, STANLEY RD, BOOTLE
166, BEDFORD RD, ROCKFERRY, 3, WALLASEY RD, LISCARD.
517, LORD ST, SOUTHPORT.

TELEGRAMS
BEES, TOXTETH, LIVERPOOL.
TELEPHONE 5020 ROYAL.

TELEPHONE &
TELEGRAMS
LIVERPOOL,
ROYAL 5020

Bees Ltd.

HEAD OFFICES,
SEED & BULB WAREHOUSES,
175-181, MILL ST
MILL STREET,
Liverpool. 12th. Oct. 14. 1914.

NURSERIES,
SEALAND, CHESTER

PRIMULA FORRESTII.
Glorious golden yellow rock plant, leaves and flowers
fragrant of ripe fruit.

As Bulley's plant and seed nursery flourished, its name changed, and its letter headings were designed to reflect its success:
(top) 1908
(middle) 1911
(bottom) 1914.

into any previous genus within this family. When studied by Balfour and his assistant, William Wright Smith, they decided to name a new genus, *Beesia*, after Bees Ltd. Balfour wrote in 1915: 'The generic name is formed from the title of the horticultural firm Bees Ltd, whose enterprise in the botanical exploration of China, Burma and the Himalayas is well known.'[31] It was a scientific accolade of gratitude. For without the fees from Bees Ltd, neither Forrest nor Ward would have begun their plant-hunting careers in south-east Asia. Forrest's new plant was named *Beesia cordata* (now *B. calthifolia*) and Ward's plant was named *B. deltophylla*. Not many people this century have had the names of two genera of plants associated with them (*Bulleyia* and *Beesia*).

The Himalayas were mentioned because, by then, Bulley had arranged for Bees Ltd to sponsor a third plant hunter, Roland Edgar Cooper. Although Bulley had described Ward's pay as a 'heavy item', Bees was thriving, and he took on Cooper as another man to move about the chess board. He sent him to hunt in the Himalayan kingdoms of Sikkim and Bhutan. It was an opportunity to tap another area of the immense reservoir of unknown plants in the Sino-Himalayan region.

6

R E Cooper in Sikkim and Bhutan

I have a man for you at any time you wish for the East (BALFOUR, 1912).[1]

Sikkim reveals problems

Cooper came as a bonus. In the autumn of 1912 Bulley still glowed in the light of Forrest's flowers, and he hoped for more from Ward. Then Cooper was wafted into view, and Bulley could not say 'no' to a promising young man with Edinburgh connections.

Roland Edgar Cooper (1890–1962) had a tragic start to life; he was orphaned at the age of three. But in his teens unusual opportunities came his way. His uncle and guardian, Mr William Wright Smith, took him to Calcutta in 1907, and from there Cooper collected plants in Sikkim and loved the experience. When they both moved to Edinburgh in 1910, contact with Bulley filled Cooper with hope …

It was a casual introduction by post, and it came at the right psychological moment. Bulley had just failed to secure a collector in the Andes. Balfour took his chance to tempt Bulley with fresh bait:

Roland Edgar Cooper (1890–1962)

> I have a man for you at any time you wish for the East. He has already done some collecting in the Himalayas. He has been through our Course of Instruction here and he has the advantage of being able to speak some of the Indian dialects. He is a thoroughly trustworthy young fellow.[2]

Ever curious, and ready to pick up chances, Bulley replied:

> Re your Collector – who and what is he? If Ward keeps his present intention, he will retire from the business in 2 years' time, and I shall want someone then. In the meantime, would your man like a shot at Alpine Lebanon?[3]

There followed a tip-top reference:

House of the curator of the herbarium, Calcutta Botanic Garden, about 1908–10, when R E Cooper (standing, left) stayed with his uncle, Mr W Wright Smith (standing, right) and Mrs Smith before he collected for A K Bulley.

… his name is Cooper … He is a youngster of 22 years who was in the Calcutta Garden when my assistant, Mr Smith, was in charge there, and he is a nephew of Mr Smith … he collected in the Himalayas for the Calcutta Garden and he has a good knowledge of the northern Indian dialects. I am told that he has an aptitude for picking up languages. He is accustomed to roughing it and is a good traveller. He wishes to go in for the life of a collector of seeds and plants … I should think that he would make an excellent collector of seeds …[4]

How could Bulley resist? Cooper sounded ideal. It might mean supporting two collectors at once. 'Shucks!' said Bulley, but an extra collector could boost Bees' sales of new and rare plants. It seemed most opportune. He had a fresh start in his staff, too. Dixon, whom Bulley praised as 'half Scotch', was keeping the new and rare plants in excellent order at Sealand, while his splendid head gardener, Hope, was at Ness. He felt well equipped to succeed with new seed.

But where to send Cooper? A friend, Siehe, offered to collect in Lebanon for him, and Bulley had 'reserved' the Karakorams for Ward. So Bulley's mind quickly ranged elsewhere, from the Altai Mountains in Mongolia to the mountains of Caucasus and the heights of Basutoland (Lesotho) in southern Africa. The latter was the favourite, but doubts existed over access and cost.

Balfour suggested the small Himalayan kingdom of Sikkim, then a protectorate of British India. It is tucked between Nepal and Bhutan and often thought of as a botanist's paradise. Kangchenjunga (8580 m) towers over the western boundary with Nepal, and lofty, snow-capped peaks almost encircle the main drainage basin of the Tista river, which flows south to the hot plains of the Brahmaputra. Climbers to the snowline go through marvellous rhododendron forests before reaching the colder, alpine conditions of the upper slopes.

The rhododendrons had been well hunted already, the pioneering work of Joseph Hooker culminating in his classic illustrated work, *Rhododendrons of the Sikkim-Himalaya* (Hooker, 1849–51). But it was hoped that the higher slopes would yield new primulas and other hardy herbaceous plants suitable for British gardens. For several years Bulley had considered having a collector in Sikkim. Already well-known garden primulas had come from there, *Primula denticulata* (drumstick primula), *P. capitata* and *P. sikkimensis*, so he had a good reason to hope for more garden treasures. He agreed happily to the idea and asked advice about pay.

When in bed with 'flu Bulley wrote to Balfour, 'This letter will be well disinfected before it goes … I suggest that the engagement be for 3 years, provided I live.'[5] He agreed to give Cooper £150 a year, also paying all expenses there and back and during the expeditions, but not between expeditions, i.e. winter and spring. It was a commitment of about £500 a year.

Bulley invited Cooper's uncle, an expert on Indian plants, to come for tea and stay a night at Ness to discuss Cooper's programme. Their chat confirmed that Cooper would start with Sikkim and then 'probably work round by Kumaon to the North West.'

Bulley met Cooper at Kew and liked him. 'Cooper is an unknown quantity, but he has given me quite a different impression [from Ward] … he seemed to care for plants only, and to have a good notion of them.'[6] Bulley was reassuring himself. He longed for Forrest's success in China to be mirrored by Cooper in the Himalaya. Maybe a new catalogue headline, 'New Primulas from the Himalayas', would happen? Cooper was younger than either Forrest or Ward, but he had had useful experience. Would the plants sell? There was every reason to be hopeful; good hardy flowers were now much prized in gardens. Gertrude Jekyll was recommending primulas as rock garden, border and bog plants.

Cooper was in Sikkim from June to October 1913. Bulley was agog for news of him. By August he had not 'struck much yet'; by September he was disappointed by his travels and reported 'nothing good'. He was a conscientious and observant botanist; he collected and dried over a thousand good-quality plant specimens, which are still a useful resource for scientists today. He discovered a new, sweet-scented primula, *Primula cooperi*, which is endemic to Sikkim, but – and here is the rub – no new showy horticultural 'winners' similar to Forrest's primulas from Yunnan. Cooper sent Bulley seed of some very beautiful, small primulas, but that is where Bulley's threefold problems began.

The majority of Cooper's Sikkim seed was collected from plants growing in rock crevices, gravel or peat on windswept glacial moraines and rock screes at altitudes of 3800–4300 m. He had collected seed up to the Sikkim watershed with Tibet, and even into Tibet. Bulley's anticipation of growing some marvellous plants was intense. 'Don't I just hope that Cooper has had luck with seed of the Soldanelloid group – especially *P. soldanelloides* which sounds as good as *P. reidii*.[7] *P. soldanelloides* is a minute plant, but a real aristocrat of the primulas. Each flowering stem, up to 4 cm high, carries one large solitary nodding and glistening white bell. No wonder Bulley wanted to grow it.

All the soldanelloid primulas have beautiful, bell-shaped flowers, and they are primarily east Himalayan, growing in the wet, high alpine regions with about six months snow cover. They are extreme specialists to this environment, and Bulley did not realise that this inevitably makes them very difficult to grow in gardens in Britain. It is a problem to reproduce relatively dry winter conditions (as under a long snow cover), followed by cool, wet, but well-drained summer conditions (equivalent to snow melt flowing through the roots). They can be the despair of specialists today, for even in an alpine house they are very short-lived, and rarely produce ripe seed. They have been described as 'the most maddeningly difficult of all primulas.'[8] Bulley had to find that out.

A second problem was taxing Bulley terribly: would tiny primulas sell, even if they could be grown? This increasing fear was shown in his reaction to the flowers of *P. sappharina*. For years Bulley had longed to see its gem-like flowers, which Sir Joseph Hooker had discovered in Sikkim. This dwarf plant is no more than 5 cm high, with a head of up to four pendant, delicate, blue-violet flowers only 5 mm long. To his great joy, Cooper collected its seeds and in April 1915 Bulley achieved his goal. In former days Bulley would have greeted the flowers with explosive ecstasy. But on that day in April, all he could say to Balfour was '*P. sappharina* is in flower. But it is too small to be of any value.'[9] His underlying business fears surfaced. It would not be suitable for the general market, and a specialised market of alpine gardeners hardly existed yet. There was a tension between wanting to introduce new plants as an ideal and wanting to make a profit. It was a dilemma he had to face. It was crucial to the future direction of Bees' business, and the future of his plant collectors.

The third problem hit Bulley from an unexpected direction. Proudly he sent Kew 304 packets of Cooper's seed, but Kew only retained 123 packets and returned the rest to Bulley. They didn't have room for any more.

Bulley was incredulous. After all his investment, and Cooper's care, it seemed a terrible waste. Indignation soared, 'It seemed to me almost a national disgrace.'[10] But coping with the flood of seeds from plant collectors was a fundamental problem for years to come. The botanic gardens became swamped, and there were few other skilled people available for the task.

Cooper's Sikkim collecting was good for science, but as a boost for Bees' new marketable hardy plant stock it seems to have failed. However, Bulley knew that a gamble does not always work! Cooper had gained experience, and Bulley was reported in good heart for sending him exploring elsewhere.

Ideas began again to bubble from the top of his head. His mind raced from the Hazara valley in Afghanistan to northern China, the Karakoram range of north-west India, and back to the Andes. But after some research he dismissed the Karakorams and Hazara, having been attracted by 'the off chance of

Bhutan'. He didn't bank much on this, but with Bulley even a very remote possibility was never ruled out, for it just might happen.

Bhutan and the 'Blooming Rajah'

'The great desirability of working Bhutan impressed itself on me,' Bulley explained to the director of Kew.[11] His queries about it had become highly focused. He had read J C White's book on *Sikkim and Bhutan* (1909). He was fascinated by Bhutan's politics, sure of its plant riches, and he realised that this isolated Himalayan kingdom had hardly been explored.

Political reasons had mainly prevented previous European entry. Only two people had done any serious botanical collecting in Bhutan: William Griffith in 1837–8, and J Claude White in 1904–7, both of them on diplomatic missions. Otherwise Bhutan remained botanically almost unknown. It presented a critical gap of knowledge of the Sino-Himalayan flora between Sikkim and south-west China. What an opportunity for Bulley! He felt it would be worth taking trouble to bring off a haul.

H H Sir Ugyen Wang-chuk, KCIE, Maharaja of Bhutan, wearing a robe of blue brocade, with the star and ribbon of the Knight Commander of the Indian Empire, given to him in 1905.

Even today, treks to Bhutan are described as going to the 'hidden kingdom'. It is a poor, sparsely populated country the size of Switzerland; a buffer state between Tibet and India, but shielded by the Himalayas. It lies east of Sikkim and its northern peaks have permanent snow and glaciers while its main rivers flow south to the Indian plains. Soaring ridges divide up the country, making east–west communication very difficult.

Early this century, there was a loose confederation of fiefdoms in Bhutan. They were ruled by governors (ponlops) with local district officers (dzongpons). There was much rivalry between the ponlops, but Ugyen Wang-chuk, the Ponlop of Tongsa Province, was a particularly wily politician who manoeuvred himself to become the most powerful ponlop in Bhutan. He then established a hereditary monarchy, becoming the first Druk Gyalpo (king) of Bhutan on 17 December 1907. He was astutely pro-British, and the very proud holder of the star and ribbon of the Knight Commander of the Indian Empire, which he was awarded by the British for his mediation during the calamitous British expedition to Lhasa, Tibet, in 1903–4. Most importantly, and unlike Sikkim, he managed to retain the independence of Bhutan. Britain recognised it as an autonomous political entity, and, as king, Ugyen Wang-chuk had the power to refuse entry to Bhutan to anyone.

Bulley had been told that a plant collector could not go into Bhutan. However, Bulley was now on a crusade. He used every contact he could muster, offering sweeteners wherever they might help. He went straight to the

(Below) *J Claude White,*
CIE, when political officer
in Sikkim.

(Bottom) *Lt Col*
A T Gage, CIE (1871–
1945). He was director of
the Botanic Garden, Calcutta,
when Bulley sought his
advice on Cooper entering
Bhutan.

directors of the botanic gardens for advice and support. After all, it was in their interests, too, and they knew him well. David Prain, then at Kew, was a long-term acquaintance who used to send him seed from Sikkim. He was an authority on the genus *Meconopsis*, and Bulley always sent him meconopses obtained by his collectors. He wrote about his latest enthusiasm in October 1913:[12]

Dear Sir David,

Cooper has been collecting in Sikkim this season. I badly want to get him into Bhutan next year. You know better than I how rich the loot of hardy plants might be. Can you get him permission either openly, or under some official pretext? If you can put it off, I promise you a pinch of seed of everything he gets …

Sincerely yours,
A K Bulley

He similarly wrote to Balfour, asking him also to discuss it with Cooper's uncle. Then he widened his enquiries to other former collectors in the Himalayas.

Some of the most experienced had the most underhand, unexpected advice. One was the previous British political officer in Sikkim, Sir Claude White, who had successfully manipulated the Maharaja of Sikkim to gain enormous power for himself. He suggested that Cooper should by-pass the Maharaja of Bhutan; that 'a good deal could be done by going in by one of the NW passes, and making a fat collection before being turned out.'[13] Major Gage, formerly of the Calcutta Botanic Garden, agreed that the best way to get into Bhutan was to be absolutely non-official. He had the bizarre idea of using a shooting party as cover for Cooper to enter Bhutan, contriving that two trained collectors from the Himalayan Lepcha people would be members of the party.[14] He thought a deal could be struck with the Calcutta Gardens, using their trained collectors in return for herbarium specimens. He suggested Cooper could even keep safely outside the Bhutan boundary whilst sending in the Lepcha collectors. Bulley was nervous.

Instead, Bulley chose to write to His Highness the Maharaja of Bhutan. He asked permission for Cooper to enter Bhutan to collect alpine plants, and grandly explained, 'that it was a service to mankind to get the fine things there must be on the Bhutan Himalaya into the gardens of the world.'[15]

He got a reply, rejoiced, and recounted the details to Balfour:[16]

(Right) **Plate 18.**
Bulleyia yunnanensis,
an orchid of a new genus
discovered by Forrest in
Yunnan and named in Bulley's
honour.

(Below) **Plate 19.**
Roscoea humeana,
discovered by Forrest. The
genus was named a century
earlier after William Roscoe,
a founder of Liverpool's first
botanic garden.

Plate 20.
Gentians were Bulley's favourite flowers. Gentiana sino-ornata was discovered by Forrest in alpine meadows at 4500 m.

Plate 21.
Gentiana trichotoma. Bees first exhibited the plant as Gentiana hopei, in honour of Bulley's head gardener, Josiah Hope. It was grown from seed collected by Ward in 1921.

(*Above*) **Plate 22.**
Gentiana prolata,
*a native of Sikkim and
Bhutan, was discovered
by Cooper in 1914.*

Plate 23.
*Gentiana farreri from
Kansu. Farrer proudly
recorded it blooming in
Edinburgh (1916) 'in
such profusion and glory
as to elicit universal
shrieks.'*

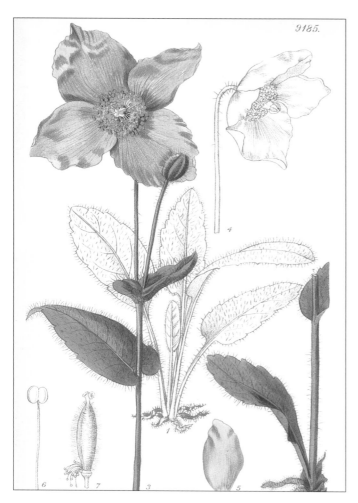

9185.

Plate 24.
Meconopsis betonicifolia, the Himalayan blue poppy. It created a sensation when introduced into cultivation by Ward in 1924.

Plate 25.
Meconopsis × sheldonii 'Slieve Donard'. This fine cultivar is a hybrid, M. betonicifolia × M. grandis.

Ness,
Neston
Cheshire
Nov. 22, 1913

Dear Dr Balfour

Great! To my surprise I have actually received a reply to my gushy letter to the Maharajah.
'From Raja Ugyen Dorzi
Agent to Maharajah of Bhutan.
With reference to your letter to the address of H.H. the Maharajah, Bhutan, requesting that Mr R.E. Cooper may be permitted to collect alpine plants on the Himalayas of Bhutan, I beg to inform you that you may apply on this subject to the Political Officer in Sikkim for a frontier pass.
Yours faithfully
(hieroglyphics)
Ugyen Dorzi'
Hoop-la!

Yours sincerely
A K Bulley

But within four days Bulley descended to the depths of gloom. Sir Claude White explained that he must still apply through the normal official channels. He had to proceed with the tiresome bureaucracy of British India, the decision for permission being shunted up slowly through the hierarchy. It was almost more than Bulley could bear as the collecting season approached.

In February 1914 Bulley wrote to Lord Morley at the India Office in London. He exhorted the directors of Kew and Edinburgh botanic gardens to do the same, 'letting him [Morley] know that I am a responsible person who will not abuse privilege ... and that the Botanic Gardens would benefit.'[17] Lord Morley had been Secretary of State for India and was then Lord President of the Council.

In his garden at Ness, Bulley was rejoicing in the rare Chilean crocus, *Tecophilea cyanocrocus*, which was flowering for its third year, and he was finding shoddy (shredded woollen rags) from the Yorkshire Mills, 'A1 for roses'. But he was also lining up Lord Morley, a political 'heavyweight' of the Empire, in his battle to gain loot from a peripheral state.

At last, it happened! In May 1914, after eight months of conniving and correspondence, Bulley received a cable: 'Bhutan entry obtained Cooper.' Bulley felt intoxicated. He was also grateful to Cooper, feeling that his groundwork with the Maharaja's agent had probably tipped the balance. He pondered on the contrast between his two collectors: 'Cooper gets into a country for which no-one else has a permit. Ward is barred (for his own folly) from one into which anyone else may go.'[18]

Thinking of the fine loot that would be his to share, he agreed that Edinburgh should receive all the herbarium specimens for identification, and the first complete set of duplicates would go to the Royal Botanic Gardens,

Calcutta, if they provided collectors. It was now up to Cooper to see what he could do.

Bulley also looked ahead and wrote to Kew: 'I wonder whether you can give me any information on a matter which is puzzling me — what I ought to give the blooming Rajah, to keep him in good humour, and secure the permit again next year. I haven't a notion.'[19] White recommended silk or woollens, Bulley thought of a heavy Inverness plaid rug. Balfour thought an Inverness cape was not a bad idea, and Smith suggested that the most 'stimulating effect' was achieved by sending a small gift immediately, followed by another later. We do not know what he gave, but the following year's permit was gained.

A world away from the war

Cooper entered south-west Bhutan on 1 July 1914 with some half-dozen Lepcha collectors and a Bhutanese escort. He felt the importance of the occasion. He had nearly five months in Bhutan ahead of him. The itinerary was to be written in an old school exercise book. On its cover the name 'George Heriot's School' was strongly crossed out and replaced by 'BHUTAN'. The 'class' heading was eliminated in favour of 'Collector for A.K. Bulley Esq.'

He planned a continuing traverse with no more than two nights in any place, except for a visit to the maharaja. He aimed to collect new plants of horticultural interest, especially in the genera *Primula* and *Rhododendron*, which were being worked on at Edinburgh by Balfour and Wright Smith. He was to collect seed for Bulley and the botanic gardens, being the first person ever to collect wild seed in Bhutan for garden trials in Europe.

The herbarium label for a dried specimen of Viburnum grandiflorum, at the Royal Botanic Garden, Edinburgh. Cooper introduced the plant to cultivation (see Plate 29).

Viburnum grandiflorum Wall. ex DC.

Det. R. A. King (RBG Edinburgh, UK)   8, 1988

FLORA OF BHUTAN.

Locality Parshong. Jimpu.
Date 28/9/14.
Altitude 12500'
Remarks No. 3023
Bush. 10'± under Conifer. Rhod.
Viburnum grandiflora

R. E. COOPER. Collector for
A. K. BULLEY. Esq.., CHESHIRE.

Claude White had written an enticing description of the vegetation which awaited Cooper: 'Between 4000 and 15000 feet [1200 and 4500 m] the whole of the higher hills are clothed with most beautiful rhododendrons ... flowering in masses, a blaze of colour, while the magnolia blossoms stand out pure white and pink ... At high elevations are the enormous pine forests into which the glaciers descend, and still higher, stretches of magnificent grazing grounds studded with alpine flowers, surrounded by some of the finest snow peaks in the world.'

Cooper relished an almost royal progress as he paid his respect to one dzongpon after another. His diplomacy contrasted with Ward's recklessness, and ensured his return the following year. He concentrated collecting in west-central Bhutan and three northern valleys, the Thimpu Chu, Mo Chu and Bumthang Chu. He explored above the tree line, to mountain passes (Plate 26) rich with alpine flowers and wonderful views far into Tibet. He collected over 2600 plant specimens. New discoveries included a gentian, *Gentiana prolata* (Plate 22), the sweet-scented *Cotoneaster cooperi*, and the hardy, fragrant, winter-flowering shrub, *Viburnum grandiflorum* (Plate 29).

The First World War broke out in Europe in August 1914, while Cooper was meeting the maharaja. He then returned to the Thimpu valley to collect seeds. They were harvested in high winds and snow storms, from 2300 to 4900 m, the plants often growing in glacial debris varying from gravel to boulders. Kew received 198 packets of these seeds from Bees a few months later. Cooper meticulously dried and cleaned the seeds, dutifully sending Bulley, as requested, 48 bottles filled with seed and carbon dioxide gas.

This was a new idea put forward at a meeting of the Royal Society earlier in the year, and reported in the *Gardeners' Chronicle*.[20] It was suggested that 30% carbon dioxide might reduce seed deterioration on long sea journeys, and might even be applied on a commercial scale. Ever keen on new ideas, Bulley decided to apply carbon dioxide to half the seed harvests of Ward and Cooper, as an experiment. Soon Bulley was reporting happily, 'Cooper's seeds have germinated remarkably well. Fully 75% are up.'[21] Three months later he was even more gleeful, 'Cooper sent me some seeds packed in bottles of carbon dioxide. Four or five kinds have germinated, which failed in ordinary treatment. The rest given by the carbon dioxide seems to amount to much the same thing as freezing.'[22] Balfour was somewhat mystified by Bulley's new game, but as polite as ever: 'What you tell me about Cooper's seeds is most interesting. How does he manage to get the carbon dioxide?' Regretfully, that is unknown, although six years later Ward was using 'sparklets' produced for fizzy drinks.

Bulley succeeded in bringing two beautiful new primulas from Bhutan into flower in 1915. One was *Primula tibetica*, whose brilliant carmine-pink flowers adorn very high slopes, growing by glaciers and runnels of melting snow. It was still in cultivation in 1928, and has been re-introduced since. The other primula was *P. menziesiana* (now considered a variant of *P. bellidifolia*), and he showed them with *P. smithiana* in London in June 1916 despite the great difficulties of wartime travel.

Cooper nearly joined the war in 1915. The first that Bulley knew of this was a cryptic telegram to Bees Ltd, saying 'Business as usual.' Bulley was puzzled but pleased, and it emerged that Cooper had been rejected by the Indian authorities for army service. He had failed a medical examination because of a tendency to cleft palate, which would not prevent him from plant collecting!

Some fascinating flowers were discovered in 1915, thanks to this reprieve. In May he discovered *Rhododendron rhabdotum* (syn. a variety of *R. dalhousiae*) (Plate 30). 'I know nothing like it,' enthused Balfour as he examined its large white flowers with striking bands of crimson, like an *Ipomoea*. Kingdon Ward later collected seeds, but it is not fully hardy, being restricted to the milder, sheltered areas of Britain.

Another spectacular find was *Lobelia nubigena*, which is horticulturally unimportant, but geographically amazing. It grows up to 1 m high, with a terminal inflorescence covered in hairy bracts. Cooper found it locally on the Yato La ridge at 4000 m in Bhutan, and it is unlike any other lobelia in Asia, Europe or North America. It seems nearest in form to the giant lobelias of the Ruwenzori Mountains of equatorial East Africa.

Success was tempered by days of profitless searching, routes being abandoned because of landslides and floods, or permission to collect being 'regretfully refused'. Cooper followed tracks that petered out, got lost in the mist, and was glad to return to the valley after 'those sodden, cold, misty and headachy' ridge tops. He did not love the wilderness in the same way as Ward; he was more pedestrian, but very determined and organised. For two weeks in June, he wrote in his itinerary 'self ill, sent men to …' as he nursed septic sores caused by scratches, leeches and insect bites. On his recovery he climbed 900 m, camped on a spur at 4000 m and was rewarded by *Lobelia nubigena*, which he photographed.

He also enjoyed trying out his linguistic skill with Raja Ugyen Dorzi, the Bhutanese prime minister with whom Bulley had corresponded. Cooper recorded,

> meeting with him was pleasurable, no interpreter being necessary. My Hindustani suitable for servants etc., was rather strained at times to make polite conversation but on the question of stores and the proposed route to Tawang we were able to understand each other fairly well I hope.[23]

The 'Tawang trip' was eastwards, over a pass called the Rudong la, where it is said yaks' horns used to jam between the rocks either side of the tortuous, steep path. It was on a slippery scree on this pass that Cooper grabbed a branch of *Buddleia cooperi*, to save his fall, and accidentally discovered this new plant! Others needed miles of determined marching to find, and further east and north they climbed up a ridge to the Narim Thang plain at 4300 m. They were near the Tibet border, encircled by glaciers and snowy peaks, with dwarf primulas at their feet, and *Primula sappharina's* dainty bells dancing in the wind. Then Cooper suddenly found *P. eburnea* (syn. *P. harroviana*) (Plate 27) by a glacier lake. It was growing in peaty soil under rocks, sheltered from the wind and rain, but open to the sun. He called it the 'gem of the whole of the eastern Himalaya'. It has been described as having ethereal beauty, with its showy cluster of 6–12, ivory-white and sweetly scented flowers, only 15 cm above the ground. Its seeds were later harvested by one of Cooper's men, and Bulley showed it in 1919, when it received an award of merit from the RHS. He was delighted, 'It has that refined combination of white and green, wh. [which] so fetches me in *P. reidii.'*[24] By 1933 it had been lost to cultivation, and did not flower in Britain again until plants were flown home in 1949, several years after Bulley died.

Other beautiful primulas introduced to Britain by Cooper's seed were *P. umbratalis*, *P. chasmophila* and the delightful, ivory-coloured flowers of *P. hopeana* (*P. sikkimensis* var. *hopeana*) which Bulley asked to be named after his head gardener, Mr Hope. But they all tend to be short-lived and not easy in cultivation.

Soon it was time to meet the maharaja before leaving Bhutan. Cooper recorded:

> After His Highness the Maharaja of Bhutan had called and chatted over tea and trouble and brought a present of brocade the Maharani and Kumar with the Kumari and her son called and were entertained to the music of three gramophones. It was dark necessitating lights and great interest was displayed in my pocket torch …[25]

The next day the maharaja was seen to be 'waving a long white scarf as farewell …' (a symbol trusting that relations would always be friendly). But Cooper was not to return again.

Clouds and silver linings

Cooper saw his botanical collections as 'little more than an occasional mouthful on the move', but they confirmed the richness of the Bhutan flora and its biogeographical interest. Horticulturally, however, the seed harvest was less successful. There were few 'gardeners' plants'. From his first Bhutanese haul, Bulley reported, 'From my point of view they are quite worthless. I feel rather 'down' on Bhutan.'[26] In January 1916 Bulley declared, 'He seems to have traversed a good deal of Bhutan, and the results seem too poor to justify further time spent there.'[27]

In the next breath, Bulley continued, 'I don't suppose Kulu – close to Simla [Shimla], and in a still drier region than Bhutan, will yield much. But it should be a change of Flora. Do you know anything about the New Guinea Flora? Is it worth a season's collecting?' He was off again, his grasshopper mind in full flight round the mountains of the world. He reconsidered eastern Bhutan, and then wrote to Cooper to ask if he would learn Chinese prior to going to Shensi, China. And he wrote unsuccessfully to the Maharaja of Nepal, asking leave for Cooper to collect there. The First World War was accelerating, but in Bulley's mind the world was still for exploring. He went to Kew and had a 'good yarn with Dr Stapf as to best hunting grounds for hardies.'[28]

However, Cooper was on course for Kulu, in the north-west Himalaya, among the snowy heights bordering on Kashmir. Bees supported him there for a season, before Cooper joined HM Forces. Fifty-nine packets of his seed were sent by Bees to Kew in 1916, and he collected another thousand plant specimens, making a total of 6000 herbarium specimens collected during his sponsorship by Bees.[29]

During these four years Bees must have invested at least £2000 in Cooper for little, if any, commercial gain. Bulley's hopes in Cooper outran the horticultural achievements. Scientific knowledge was the most immediate beneficiary. But the long-term view gives a picture of a pioneer discovering new plants and providing information beneficial to later plant collectors such as Frank Ludlow and George Sherriff, and discovering beautiful new alpines which have lured collectors back to the Himalyas time and time again.

When gloom and doubts engulfed Bulley, he blamed himself for casualties in growing his collectors' plants. Balfour would have none of this. 'Misfortunes befall gardening everywhere, and who does not lose plants which others manage to keep.' After all, that was why the seed was always shared. He reminded Bulley that it was thanks to his sponsorship that any of the new flowers were in cultivation. 'The record of what you have done for horticulture has yet to be written and none will be more glorious … We here prosper on your liberal gifts.'[30] 'All right,' replied Bulley, 'We'll call it a draw, and continue collaborating for the general benefit of mankind!'

The war catches up with them

The First World War was like a vortex, sucking people into it, destroying whole families and shattering their dreams. Bulley was fortunate that none of his family was killed and he adapted to maintain his garden and businesses. He was determined to keep the illusion of 'business as usual' and never mentioned the war in his botanical correspondence. He never lost 'delight in momentariness' of a flower, and always had plans in store. But the tragedies of war were inescapable, they affected him deeply, and some were very near home.

Liverpool was the home of the *Lusitania*, the largest, fastest, and most powerful steamer on the North Atlantic run. It was sunk by a German U-boat on 7 May 1915 and over 1200 men, women and children died. Anti-German riots followed. Before all the dead had been buried, Bulley attended a Fabian Conference on 'The Terms of Peace' at Barrow House, Keswick. Bernard Shaw and Mr and Mrs Sydney Webb and many others were there to discuss possible international machinery for the prevention of future wars.

A reassuring message after the outbreak of the First World War.

From Keswick Bulley journeyed on to Edinburgh and enjoyed the botanic garden as if nothing else was happening. But inevitably the war soon affected his plans. Although Cooper was safe in Bhutan the fruits of his labours were threatened.

The first calamity was in early September 1914. 'We have just got news of the loss of a consignment from Cooper – gone to the bottom of the Indian Ocean in the *City of Westminster* sunk by the Germans.'[31] Many later plant specimens from Bhutan had to be stored in Calcutta until some years after the war. They were neglected in out-houses, eaten by insects, and some reduced to powder. It was the 1950s before all Cooper's dried specimens had been studied in Edinburgh.

Plant propagation suffered, too. Lord Kitchener's recruitment drive, 'Your King and Country Need You', led to a chronic lack of skilled manpower.

At Edinburgh, Balfour lost 60 men within the first month of war. By 1917 he admitted, 'I have not a man looking after my plants who would have been allowed to come near them in the old days.' At Kew, 77 members of staff were serving in HM Forces by April 1915, yet Bees sent Kew 250 packets of seed from Ward and Cooper that year. Was it possible to do justice to their seeds? Kew had insufficient room before the war; now they also had too few skilled staff.

Bees' policies had to be changed; more seeds for food, and only the 'commonest truck' of garden flowers in wartime. As the lights flickered and went out all over Europe, the number and variety of available ornamental seed, plants and cut flowers were curtailed. Bees' florist shops on Merseyside declined from a peak of six to two, and by 1916–17 sales of vegetable seeds were over twice the value of flower seeds. Bees now had coloured illustrations in its catalogues to entice and delight its customers, but only some of Forrest's early-collected successes, and a few new crosses, such as 'Primula bulleyana X P. beesiana', were well established in the market place. 'New Beesian Primulas' sold well, but it was increasingly difficult to sell 'new and rare' plants. So as the war continued into its third year it seemed commercial folly to continue to spend £500 or £600 a year on Cooper.

Bulley was torn. He wanted to continue: in August 1916 he heard that Cooper had found three forms of Isopyrum (Paraquilegia) including I. microphyllum 'a perfect gem', and the next month Balfour reported, 'He [Cooper] has some nice plants. One, a white-flowered creeping dwarf … should be a fine rock-plant.' But Bulley had to face reality. He made his decision. In October 1916 he wrote to Cooper that he feared he could not see the way forward for more than one season, but that he did not want to 'let him down with a bump'. He asked what Cooper's thoughts were.

Balfour had predicted that Cooper was so keen on collecting that he would continue until 'his half century at least'. But Cooper enlisted for the war, and he never returned to full-time plant hunting. It was a turning point for Bulley, too. His leading role in plant introduction had to be subjugated to the exigencies and realities of war. His hopes and ambitions were wounded. Bees stopped sending seeds to Kew for three years after Cooper's last batch in February 1917. Indeed, it was the First World War which brought Bees' sole sponsorship of plant hunters to a premature end. Never again was he to invest so heavily in one expedition.

However, death alone would halt Bulley's passion for plants! His letters to Balfour were packed with happy details of Cooper's latest plants in flower and plans for future expeditions. He remained resilient and innovative. He even continued small wartime speculations on plant hunting. More importantly, he had begun sponsorship within a syndicate, and that form of patronage was to recontinue after the war. Bulley's role in syndicates began with part-sponsorship of a famous and influential rock gardener, Reginald Farrer. They had a fraught relationship, but it produced some wonderful garden plants.

～ 7 ～

Reginald Farrer in China and Burma

In no sphere more than in plant collecting does appetite grow!
(BALFOUR, 1915)[1]

Farrer joins the hunt

By the spring of 1913 a famous rock gardener was casting an envious eye on the plant collectors in China. This was Reginald Farrer (1880–1920).

Aged 33 and already experienced in collecting and growing alpine plants of Europe, he was the last to join in this golden age of British plant collecting in south-east Asia, before the First World War closed in. He did not intend to involve Bulley, but force of circumstances gradually took over until Bulley became the key person in his mind for funding, his only hope in trouble.

Farrer lived in the comfort and style of the gentry in a large and gracious mansion, Ingleborough Hall, on a country estate of 40 000 acres in the West Riding of Yorkshire. The family lived elegantly, hosted house parties and moved in Liberal circles. Farrer was artistic, had a taste for fine things and quality clothes. As a boy, poor health prevented him from going to Eton, but he went to Balliol College, Oxford and then developed an interest in politics, wrote novels, travelled to Ceylon (Sri Lanka) and Japan and converted to Buddhism. But alpine flowers were his abiding passion and his rock garden at home included specially constructed moraines and a high cliff planted with precious alpine plants, many of them personally collected. He was an expert on European primulas and was experimenting on the recently introduced species. He had started the Craven Nursery to profit from the increasing interest in rock garden and alpine plants, even before Bulley started Bees Ltd. Now, like Bulley, he wanted to make a commercial *coup* by selling newly discovered plants, and in a way that Bulley had dreamed of, but never undertook, Farrer wanted to plant-hunt in China himself. And, no doubt, he dreamed of having at least a few newly discovered plants named, forever, '*Farreria*'…

Reginald John Farrer (1880–1920)

Farrer stood out in the world of Edwardian horticulture. He was recognised as a leader in alpine gardening and everyone knew him through his writing. His most popular book, *My Rock Garden* (1907), made him a celebrity and by 1913 he was writing his third book on rock gardening (*The English Rock Garden*). He wrote frequently on alpine plants in the weekly *Gardeners' Chronicle*. He was a theatrical character and his plant descriptions were lyrical, sometimes 'over the top', but immensely readable and influential. When Bulley read his description of *Lithospermum erythrorhizon*, he wrote 'According to Farrer's account it must be a ripping good thing with its large azure blue flowers,' and he enquired of Balfour whether it could be obtained from the Tokyo Botanic Garden.[2]

Bulley was nearly 20 years senior to Farrer. Despite Farrer's high profile in rock gardening circles, Bulley was well able to stand up to him if he felt the need. For example, in February 1910 Farrer had tried to overwinter *Primula forrestii* for the first time. He reported in the *Gardeners' Chronicle* that 'I can already see that I must mourn – and bitterly indeed – for glorious *P. forrestii*.'[3] Bulley wanted to exhibit this and other new primulas and to profit from selling them in large numbers. Under the name of Bees Ltd he politely and pointedly replied, 'We regret that Mr. Reginald Farrer had to mourn the loss of his plant. Perhaps our experience, as introducers of this and other new Primulas of last season, may help to prevent further losses.'[4] He cited the trial beds at Sealand where *P. forrestii* was quite hardy; it was injured by excessive moisture, but a large batch was growing successfully on a raised and dry bed out of doors in the shelter of a wood. Round One, one all!

It was inevitable that the paths of Farrer and Bulley should cross. They were rivals at shows and in the nursery trade. They often exhibited and competed side by side in the same alpine and rock garden sections. When Farrer donated two silver cups to the RHS, Bees was the first to win the 'Farrer Cup' which was awarded for six new and rare dwarf rock plants.[5]

They respected each others' skills and visited each others' gardens; they had a common bond in their love of alpines; but their strong, contrasting personalities and different social backgrounds led to an uneasy rapport. Farrer mixed with the establishment of the horticultural world, being a member of the élite and exclusive Horticultural Club whose members met at the Hotel Windsor in London for monthly dinner and talks. Bulley would never even be considered for this, nor would he have wanted to attend. But to Farrer this gave extra status and he must have felt well-placed to wield influence and impress in finding funding for a trip to China. It was all the more a blow to his pride when later he had to plead with Bulley for help. When Bulley was due to meet Farrer's mother, Farrer felt bound to warn her, 'You won't much like him, but you won't be bothered by him. Nor does he drink anything.'

In 1913 Farrer befriended William Purdom, a Kew-trained gardener who had just returned from plant-hunting in Kansu on the Tibetan border of north-west China. Purdom was eager to return to Kansu, he could speak Chinese and had the 'know how' in China, and together they began excitedly to hatch plans go to there. Balfour also encouraged Farrer to go to Kansu, as two Russian army officers, Przewalski and Potanin, had been there and collected plants which looked promisingly hardy for British gardens. The Tsin-ling range was still 'uncreamed' and waiting for them. Furthermore, collecting in the north of China avoided any potential jealous clash with Forrest or Ward who were both searching further south in the mountains of Yunnan, Szechuan (Sichuan) and neighbouring Tibet. Farrer was exultantly happy to have this all decided and felt ready to 'hop on my feet to be off.'[6]

However, it was not as easy as that. Farrer's father held tightly to the purse strings of the Ingleborough estate. Farrer had a personal allowance which he never thought was adequate to live as a gentleman should; certainly it would not be enough for an expedition. At first Farrer had grand ideas of a government grant but money was tight there, too. Farrer's chances were diminished because he was not science-trained and the directors of the botanic gardens did not give him their backing for a grant. Bulley offered to hire him but was snubbed by Farrer at the time, when his pride was against being a 'mere hired collector' for Bulley. So Farrer resorted to setting up a syndicate of supporters who would give him money in return for a share of the seeds. He obtained some dozen subscribers but Bulley was not amongst them so he was not expectant as Farrer and Purdom set off for the promised land in early 1914, in time for the flowering season in Kansu.

Bulley was preoccupied with his own affairs and collectors. His cotton business was expanding its premises in Liverpool, and his new head gardener, Mr Josiah Hope, was transforming the gardens at Ness, Bees' Nursery having been moved to a larger site. He was already overstretched trying to keep up with the propagation of his own collectors' seeds. Moreover, Bees was still proudly exhibiting Forrest's new plant introductions. As Farrer was feeling the thrill of the hills in China, the hardy flowering plants section at the 1914 Chelsea Show included the new Chinese plants of Messrs Bees Ltd. The *Gardeners' Chronicle* reported:

> Messrs. Bees, Ltd, Liverpool, made a valuable exhibit of the best things that we owe to the Chinese collections of Forrest. *Primula secundiflora, Roscoea cautleoides, Incarvillea brevipes* and the dwarf silver-leaved *Potentilla fruticosa nana argentea*, which is new, stood out as conspicuously good.[7]

Primula secundiflora gained an award of merit and Bees Ltd was awarded the Silver-Gilt Banksian Medal for Alpines. A month later, after the RHS Exhibition at Holland House, in July 1914, Bulley must have smiled at the following report:

> Messrs. Bees Ltd, Sealand, Chester, showed some good Delphiniums and hardy herbaceous plants, but it was their new and rare plants that gave distinction and quality to their collection ... These plants enabled one to overlook the fact that the 'rocks' were made of cork.[8]

The Silver Floral Medal, however, was awarded and Bulley had enjoyed experimenting with a new substrate, even if the judges were not amused.

Maybe it was this continuing appreciation of Bees' new and rare plants which tempted Bulley to change his mind over Farrer. The First World War was only weeks ahead, but few people had any idea of its imminence, and could not possibly foresee its catastrophic effects. The outlook for a market in alpine plants looked expansive. There was increasing national interest in rock gardening and Bees' new plants were getting good coverage in botanic gardens' reports. Balfour at Edinburgh announced his indebtedness for candelabra primulas (see Plates 11 and 13); from Dublin came mention of a new michaelmas daisy, *Aster batangensis*, which flowered in May/June and was introduced by Bees. The Cambridge Botanic Garden reported 'choice additions' including *Jasminum beesianum* (Plate 15), *Iris forrestii*, *I. bulleyana*, *Aconitum bulleyanum* and *Delphinium bulleyanum*. It was all good advertisement and an encouragement for Bulley, and to cap it all at the end of the year, an article on eight slipper orchids of the 'China-Tibetan Borderland' ended 'We ought to be grateful indeed to the explorers who have beautified our gardens by the introduction of these extraordinary plants and to the firms whose enterprise sent them forth.'[9] Well! That included Bees! What an impetus for Bulley to continue his enterprise and join in sponsorship of Farrer. He wrote to Farrer in far-off Kansu, offering a share in Farrer's second collecting season in exchange for seeds.

Meconopsis quintuplinervia, the harebell poppy. This photograph was taken by Purdom in the alps of Kansu, China.

Bulley offers his sponsorship

Farrer kept the public's attention by writing six articles in the *Gardeners' Chronicle* in the autumn of 1914 describing his exploits. One can imagine Bulley's alert eye scanning these reports and picking out tempting bits of information. Farrer was finding a 'dazzling firmament' of lithospermums, one of Bulley's favourite flowers. He was enjoying *Meconopsis quintuplinervia* 'of swan-like grace ... as its blue dewdrops swing and sway all up the long Alpine slope' and Farrer hoped to re-introduce it to Britain. Moreover, he had been the first Westerner to see a truly wild, white-flowered mouton, or tree peony. If Farrer could find this long-sought flower in Kansu, what other hardy plants might lie in wait for his keen eyes? And hints of profits were openly displayed by describing a 'woodland dense with seven-and-sixpences.'

By then there was news, too, of Farrer's two mule-loads of seed packets at the end of the first season, new primulas and the exciting first discovery in the wild of the fragrant, winter-flowering *Viburnum farreri* (syn. *V. fragrans*). Bulley renewed his offer. But correspondence with Farrer went on for months, and in March 1915, Bulley wrote to Balfour, 'I am barneying with Farrer for a quarter of next season's loot. Can't say whether it will come to anything.'[10] Balfour encouraged him, 'He [Farrer] has got some really good things even on the vile loess which covers South Kansu – but he goes North to Tatung this season, when his harvest should be greater.'[11]

It was now only a matter of how much Bulley should invest in the second season of Farrer's expedition. However, it was a battle between two strong personalities each with an entrepreneurial streak and vested interests. Moreover, the ground was shifting under their feet as the First World War affected their positions. Bulley could bargain *ad infinitum* and the outcome was rather a sideline in his life at this stage. His calculating, bargaining, business instinct, sharpened from years of brokering, seemed utterly ruthless to Farrer for whom more was at stake as time went on ...

In December 1914, Farrer started confidently, writing to his mother, 'as Bulley continues urgent for a share for Bees, I am offering him half of my own for £400!' and Farrer was altogether looking for 'quite a pretty penny of profit' on his expedition. But as the 'barneying' continued, the war was accelerating. There was a growing shortage of gardeners and a decreasing market for alpine plants, and from the wilds of Kansu, Farrer heard from his mother that the family Craven Nursery was in financial trouble. This came as a thunderbolt to Farrer, and feeling powerless and fretful he replied, 'The only present help in trouble lies in A.K. Bulley.' Farrer needed cash desperately to clear the overdraft and wind up the nursery. He upped his offer of seeds to Bulley, 'offering him shares in the 2 seasons for £700, to be paid at once,' and ordered his manager to make lump-sales of his nursery stock. 'I shall certainly be able to make of the Chinese plants ... I might even offer A.K.B. a monopoly for "£1000 or £2000".'

They were hopeful dreams at a terrible time for Farrer and he had no idea how Bulley would react to any offer. He told Bulley, 'I am quitting the [nursery] business, and want only to keep 5% of the plants for my own garden.' Farrer was utterly miserable. He was far away in Kansu, imagining 'all those Chinese treasures sprouting up' at home, only to be dug up – 95% of them – and sent to Bulley. To make things worse, he felt that this second season in Kansu had been a failure so far, and he needed to collect a spectacular amount of good seed to redeem it.

Bulley disappointed Farrer. He didn't want any nursery plants, and offered Farrer only half the cash of his latest demand of £1200. Farrer confided to his mother:

> He clearly thinks he has me in a cleft stick, and is driving the hardest bargain he can – a bargain I should spit upon ... but which, as it is, I see nothing for it but to accept. ... He offers '£600 for 95% of all my own germinations of last year, and all my own seed-share of this year, exclusive of forest trees.'

Farrer cabled and wrote acceptance of the deal, even though he felt that Bulley was taking undue advantage of him. But worse was to come for Farrer ... Bulley halved that offer later! On 26 August 1915, at least a year after the 'barneying' first began, Farrer wrote, 'I've heard again from Bulley, bitten in conscience about so grinding the face of the poor, and reverting to an early offer.' In the end Farrer said he would accept any one of three suggestions, and while waiting for the reply he clung desperately to the hope of the highest sum, admitting to his mother that 'everything hinges on Bulley' concerning his plans. Bulley chose the cheapest deal which was £300. It was a fiasco for Farrer who, in a depressed mood, tried to think of another person who might step in as a shareholder and thus have a chance of 'wiping Bulley's eye.'

It appears that Bulley gave good reasons for reducing his financial involvement, for in a better frame of mind Farrer seemed to understand the plight that Bulley was feeling as a result of the escalation of the war. 'Poor Bulley, I can't blame him for so desperately wriggling in his bargain, in the present state of things ... I feel we are to be congratulated on having got even £300 out of him as things stand.' It was 1916 and the First World War was changing the situation for everyone. Bulley was withdrawing from keeping Cooper, and now he was retracting on Farrer.

The truth was that Bulley, like Farrer, was having dreams shattered. He found that his idea of selling new Chinese plants through Bees was 'utter moonshine. There is no demand.'[12] He was running down his New and Rare Plants Department because it was not profitable. He might as well give the seeds away. By May 1916 there was conscription in Britain and at the front-line trenches at the Battle of the Somme young men were being slaughtered in their thousands. That April there was only six weeks' supply of grain in Britain. Food was the priority and Bees increased its efforts in the production of vegetable seeds. Bulley even grew cereals at Ness.

In November 1916, Farrer's manager reported that Bulley was overwhelmed by the share of Farrer's seed sent to his Sealands Nursery, but that Bulley 'has evidently sent that share to the R.H.S. for free distribution to the Members!' That was unheard of before. Formerly there had been a small coterie of nurserymen and wealthy gardeners – the fortunate few – who received their share of new seeds, and, maybe, shared them with their friends. Bulley's action was indicative of times to come, when wealth or social position would no longer dictate who received the seeds. With the advent of war, the demise of gardeners and market, any keen gardener with a little space could grow Bulley's free seed from China.

Meanwhile the healing of the relationship between Farrer and Bulley took time, as shown by a comment to Balfour nearly a year later. It concerned one of the greatest treasures of Farrer's expedition, *Gentiana farreri* (Plate 23).

Balfour rejoiced in it: 'I used to think *G. sino-ornata* with its king's blue flowers was superb. This [*G. farreri*] is superbissima, and has a prospect of being a real Farrerian legacy to horticulture. I know nothing like it.'[13] In the midst of war such new and beautiful flowers brought special joy. When a famous gardener of the day, Mrs Martineau, visited Edinburgh she remarked that it was 'growing quite happily not a hundred yards away from a munition factory that was belching forth fumes and smoke.'[14] The sheer beauty of its luminous quality of blue, in these conditions, brought forth wonder. The delighted Farrer had seen high mountain passes where solid sheets of its trumpets abounded in mid-September. He asked, if it wasn't in flower at home, if he could cadge some from the Edinburgh garden because 'It would really be *too* bitter to have to buy them from Bees!'[15]

But this bitterness was only skin-deep, for seven months later – soon after his return – Farrer was visiting Bulley at Ness. One person who probably helped to bring them together was E A Bowles, a fine man and keen gardener who had collected with Farrer in the Alps, before Farrer even thought of venturing to China. Bulley wrote to him when stimulated by three witty and learned books which Bowles wrote in the early years of the war. Bulley's letter was written with such freshness that one would never guess at the wranglings he had with Farrer. They belonged to his other business side of life, whereas this exemplifies the exuberant, lively man not slow to ask a favour.

> Dear Mr Bowles,
>
> I have just finished the 3rd part of your trilogy. It goes without saying that the whole thing has been a great pleasure to me. I know some of your favourites; but of others I am quite ignorant.
>
> Now, I want to ask a favour. May I see your garden? I don't mean in the way of a single visit. I generally come to London for the fortnightly [RHS] meeting. And after seeing the Exhibition I am apt to go on to Kew. But I now know Kew pretty well, and life is short. May I, say about once a month during the flowering season, walk about your garden on a Tuesday afternoon, and look at things?[16]

Visits began the following spring, and Bulley must have shared in the joy of Farrer's harvest of seeds growing at Bowles's garden at Myddleton House, Enfield. For example, *Rosa elegantula* (syn. *R. farreri*) was growing from Kansu hips, and propagation of this and other fruits and seeds rested heavily on the botanic gardens and the relatively few gardeners of this level of expertise.

New beginnings

When Farrer visited Ness in May 1917 he found Bulley planning how they might co-operate when the war was over. Farrer was temporarily diverted by work in the Department of Information, which included writing graphic reports on the horrors of the battlefields in France, but he was writing, too, about his Chinese expedition, in his book *On the Eaves of the World*, and he was eager to discuss another trip. Bulley was in the same mood. On a spring day Farrer was welcomed, shown round the garden, involved in happy discussions of the future and given the use of the desk which was always reserved in the drawing room for guests. He wrote on Ness notepaper to Balfour, 'Bulley tells me he has already consulted you as to the most likely new collecting ground for our united forces and finances.'[17] Their love of alpines was bringing them together again; they were two of the select band of gardeners of what Farrer called 'the true persuasion'. There was no rivalry for a market for alpine plants, because they both knew that it had ceased to exist. That was not their driving force. Instead, their shared love of alpines and their genuine desire to find more of them, simply gave them a common purpose with no barneying or haggling, but new expectations of a new expedition. For this they needed each other and they needed the advice of their joint mentor, Balfour. He knew that 'You [Farrer] and Mr Bulley want fine-flowered alpines' and he suggested that the best place away from Forrest's garnerings and with the maximum hope of choice alpines would be in the unexplored triangle of high hills lying between Tibet, Burma and Yunnan, using the frontier station of Putao in Burma as a base. Ward had collected from the nearby vicinity of Hpimaw and nearly every one of his plants was new; those from the alps should be hardy and Balfour foresaw fine results.[18]

Bulley, Bowles and Balfour were invited to Ingleborough to talk over the objectives of the next expedition. Farrer was obsessed by the fear that he might tread on the toes of Forrest or Ward, intruding into territory which they regarded as theirs, but Balfour assured him that 'Twenty men working for twenty years won't exhaust it.' The expedition would set off immediately after the war ended. Bulley promised that he would be happy to have a share in a syndicate. Indeed, he was as buoyant and happy as anyone in the kingdom, because the end of the war would enable renewed plant collecting in the East. After all the pent-up frustrations of the war, Bulley's adrenalin was flowing fast in anticipation, excitement was surging forth like champagne from an uncorked bottle. How well he could understand the poem of Siegfried Sassoon, celebrating the Armistice: [19]

> Everybody suddenly burst out singing,
> And I was filled with such delight
> As prisoned birds must find in freedom …

Think of the wonderful prospect for the plant hunters: Forrest was continuing in Yunnan, Ward would be returning to Burma, Farrer was off again and plans for Cooper were developing … and Bulley was sponsoring them all. Indeed he was so enthusiastic that he arranged a syndicate of sponsors for Cooper before he had even checked whether Cooper wanted or was free to go! He had the promise of £1100 from a total of seven shareholders before Cooper declared that he was not free, and the whole thing fell through. But Bulley had shares in three expeditions, all to different areas, so the outlook was good.

Bulley's reaction to the war also took another form. Siegfried Sassoon accepted the literary editorship of the newly published *Daily Herald*, and in 1920 Bulley was to send this paper £500. In those days, wrote Robert Graves, in *Goodbye to All That*, 'The *Daily Herald* was not respectable, but violently anti-militarist.'[20]

Farrer set sail for the East on 30 January 1919 with a new companion, Euan H M Cox. Sadly it was to be Farrer's last and fatal expedition, beset with difficulties from the beginning. His movements were restricted by the local authorities and he did not reach Putao after all; he had to make Hpimaw his base, where collecting by Forrest and Ward meant a reduced likelihood of new species for Farrer. Ironically, Forrest's collectors came over the pass from Yunnan and Ward was on a neighbouring range so Farrer became extra nervous that he would find nothing new. But it was Farrer who found the beautiful Nomocharis farreri (syn. N. pardanthina var. farreri) at 3000–3350 m on the Hpimaw pass. Millions of them covered the alpine slopes and made everything

seem worthwhile. He described it as a 'spectacle of unsurpassed beauty and charm,' and he was so enraptured that he took up his paint brush and captured its beauty in watercolours. He introduced it to cultivation in Britain.

But financial troubles were never far away for Farrer. When he arrived in Upper Burma he found that prices had risen and the rupee had also risen in relative value. He wrote pleadingly to Wright Smith at Edinburgh to work up more financial support for him, and later admitted that he was running out of money for wages, running expenses and a return mule convoy.

Bulley must have received several packets of Farrer's seed in 1919 and a consignment of 82 packets of seeds arrived in February 1920, but Bulley was very slow to pay his due. Eventually, 18 months after Farrer set off, Bulley paid up in June 1920. Farrer wrote to his mother, 'A.K.B. has shoved in £200 but in such a way that only the prudence of grey hairs prevents my shoving it straight back.' He felt insulted because Bulley sent the money 'as a sort of dole',[21] and not in return for any more seed. Their fragile friendship was stretched again. Cox had returned home and Farrer was stuck in

NOMOCHARIS PARDANTHINA var. FARRERI. F.1031.

Nomocharis farreri, *discovered and painted in Burma by Farrer.*

his dripping tent, depressed by endless rain and loneliness, furious that Bulley did not even want his seeds and frustrated by Bulley's late payment. He became ill and weak and died a few months later. Aged only 40, his health could not stand up to the rigours of plant collecting in the appalling weather of those remote hills. Motivated by excitement in the hunt, but dogged by problems, Farrer's passionate quest for new alpine plants cost him his life. He was buried in the Burmese hills. (Plate 31, depicting Nomocharis aperta, was painted by Farrer just six weeks before his death.)

Farrer lives on as he would have wished, in his books and paintings and in the flowers which he introduced to our gardens. *Gentiana farreri* (Plate 23) was awarded a first-class certificate that same year and some 30 plants bear his name.[22] His book, *Rainbow Bridge*, was published posthumously, and in it he encourages his readers to grow the plants which he hunted. He extolls the charm and beauty of the harebell poppy, *Meconopsis quintuplinervia*, so that its popularity would be ensured and 'you may all see the point of raising seed.' Farrer garden favourites today include *Buddleja alternifolia*, *Geranium farreri* (Plate 8), *Clematis macropetala* and *Daphne tangutica*.

A K Bulley pacing the drawing room about the time that Farrer died.

Bulley as patron to Farrer

In the lateness of his payment, Bulley emerges as an enigma. The timing seemed casual and insensitive to Farrer, yet if it had not reached Farrer before he became ill and died, Bulley would have been mortified. On the other hand, Bulley's other activities meant that the interests of his plant hunters were not always uppermost in his mind, especially when he was not totally responsible for them, as in this case. In May 1920, before Farrer died, Bulley promised to send Bowles some plants in the autumn, asking for a reminder if they were not sent. 'I pray then without fail to let me know; for the failure will be due, not to lack of good will, but to lack of memory.'[23]

Bulley had the means to pay Farrer more. He was not short of money. The wartime inflation of cotton prices reached its peak in New York and Liverpool in February 1920. By sponsoring three plant hunters at once Bulley was indulging in his favourite hobby, riding his luck as cotton prices soared. When it arrived, his payment to Farrer was the promised sum, a £100 subscription share per year, which was usual for many expeditions, though Bulley had suggested shares of £150 for his proposed Cooper expedition in December 1918. No other person paid more on Farrer's expedition and Bulley evidently did not feel inclined to be more generous. This puzzled and frustrated Farrer, who would have liked a more open purse. But a shareholder in a syndicate normally received seeds in proportion to the payment, and Bulley did not want and could not cope with any more seeds. He was growing seeds from Forrest and Ward as well!

Bulley had a finer business sense than Farrer, enabling Bees to continue during the war, partly thanks to adaptability and diversification in the plants and seeds the firm produced. Bulley was a business man to his fingertips, and a sharp one at that. When collectors were dependent on his financial sponsorship, they saw this side of his character. But although Bulley sometimes seemed mean to Farrer, and to Forrest before him, there is no hint that Ward or Cooper complained. The frugal Ward even saved on what Bees paid him.

Bulley could change his mind lightly, seemingly unaware of the effect this had on others. It was as if blinkered vision descended on him. So, when Forrest sent home far more seeds than had been expected, Bulley panicked, searched for another gardener, and cancelled his quota of seeds from Farrer ... much to Farrer's disgust. To Bulley it was probably a sensible decision as he had such a high opinion of Forrest's ability to send back good, mature, well-dried seeds. Bulley's dilemma in receiving too many seeds was not uncommon. The burden of plant propagation still rested on too few experts.

Farrer's experience highlights the critical importance of Bulley as a sponsor of plant hunters. It wasn't easy, even for a person of Farrer's standing, to rustle up enough funds for a plant-hunting expedition. Bulley's combination of wealth from cotton and love of alpines meant money was available when it was desperately needed, even if the plant hunters themselves would have liked more!

A year after Farrer's death, Bulley became involved in a peculiarly British endeavour. It was 1921 and his long love affair with the plants of the Sino-Himalaya took a new turn. This time the expedition was not the brainchild of any botanist or gardener. Originally it did not even consider plant hunting as one of its aims. But Bulley was a catalyst for change and brought a new perspective.

8

Everest and After

The Mt. E. expedition gives an opportunity of getting into cultivation beautiful hardy wild flowers (BULLEY, 1922).[1]

Influence on the reconnaissance

When Bulley opened his newspaper on the morning of 25 February 1921, he saw instinctively what he wanted to do. There was an appeal for money to support a reconnaissance for an assault on Mt Everest, the highest mountain in the world (8848 m). It was an irresistible opportunity. A new chapter of exploration was beginning in the Himalayas, and Bulley wanted a part in this. He liked to 'think big', and saw the possibilities for new seed ... In some ways it was a giant gamble, but it was a hunch after years of experience. Altogether it was completely in character, an impulsive, entirely 'Bulley' thing to do. How could he refuse?

Mount Everest bestrides the frontier between Nepal and Tibet. Nepal was closed to foreigners, but in 1920 the Viceroy of India and the Dalai Lama of Tibet gave permission for a British expedition to approach Mt Everest from the north. The expedition was organised by the Royal Geographical Society and the

A K Bulley reading the Manchester Guardian in the drawing room at Ness.

Alpine Club. A special Tibetan passport was issued on a piece of grass paper with the Prime Minister's red seal, ordering the dzongpons and headmen to assist the sahibs by day or by night when they passed through their lands. The aim was to explore and map Mt Everest in preparation for a full assault on the summit in 1922. It was a great adventure, for everyone knew that the final ascent would involve high risks and severe hardships, the summit being 1200 m higher than anyone had ever yet ascended on any mountain. On the reconnaissance they would be in country never before seen by Europeans. They knew very little of its geography, the exact position of valleys and mountain ranges was unknown and they had only a distant picture of the northern ridge. No European had ever studied the vegetation.

The appeal in the *Manchester Guardian* was for money to finance the cost of equipment. Bulley wrote off the same day to Sir Francis Younghusband, the President of the Royal Geographical Society, London.[2]

> *Ness*
> *Neston*
> *Nr. Birkenhead*
> *Feb. 25 '21*
>
> *President*
> *Royal Geog. Soc.*
> *Dear Sir,*
>
> I have just read in the *Manchester Guardian* your appeal for funds in connection with the Mt. Everest attempt.
>
> My interest lies in alpine plants. Will there be any botanist attached to the expedition? And will it be on the mountain late enough for seeds to be secured?
>
> If so, and if I can have a share of the seeds, I will subscribe £100.
>
> *A K Bulley*

As if to substantiate the normality of his offer, Bulley appended extra information: 'Kingdon Ward, one of your members, has just sailed for China, to collect seeds of alpine plants for Mr R. Cory and myself.' (Ward was well known in geographical circles, and was currently borrowing some of their survey equipment.) Bulley was 60 years old, but his desire to find new plants was as strong as ever. He had sent out Kingdon Ward a decade ago and was still subscribing to his exploits; now he was trying a new gambit.

The Mount Everest Committee had never thought of collecting seeds. Without Bulley's initiative, it would not have happened. But Bulley had a knack of making things happen. The Mount Everest Committee was bowled over by his handsome offer, when most subscribers were only sending one or two guineas to the appeal, and discussed Bulley's proposal at their next meeting. There was no special botanist on the expedition. Dr A F R Wollaston, a distinguished explorer and member of the Alpine Club, was to be the team's doctor, mountaineer and naturalist. However, the expedition planned to be on the mountain about three months, until driven down by the winter, so – yes – seed collection and seed sharing should be possible.

Once Bulley had offered money in exchange for seeds, the idea took off. Wollaston invited Major Lionel de Rothschild to subscribe £100 for a share of plants and seeds of every rhododendron, magnolia and any other fine tree or shrub. Not to be outdone, the Royal Horticultural Society offered £100 for plants and seed, and the botanic gardens of Kew, Edinburgh and Glasnevin were to be given seed to increase the chance of germination.

Bulley did not stop there. He suggested that the expedition should use two local Lepcha people already trained by the Darjeeling Botanic Garden: 'They are accustomed to the collection of alpine seeds, and will easily multiply ten fold the botanical value of the expedition.'[3] Bulley had received seed collected by them, via the botanic garden in Calcutta, and they had helped Cooper. Wollaston duly hired some on arrival in India, and Bulley's subscription helped pay for them.

Lepcha collector holding Saussurea, a plant whose centre is as snug as cotton wool and provides shelter for bumble bees.

The expedition set out from Darjeeling in springtime, marching through the forests of Sikkim and up the Chumbi valley, the steep hillsides ablaze with the flowers of rhododendrons of every size, form and colour. Even in rain and fog they were magnificent, from the large *Rhododendron falconeri* and *R. thomsonii* to the smaller *R. campylocarpum* which was first found by Hooker. The best-flowering specimens were marked with the intention of collecting their seeds in the autumn. As the expedition ascended above 4000 m dwarf rhododendrons covered the mountainside like purple heather until higher in Tibet, for scores of miles, they could hardly see any plant more than a few centimetres high. But even at 6000 m, on a sunny terrace of stones between two glaciers, a few flowers existed.

The expedition caught people's imagination. Cablegrams to *The Times* and monthly reports in the Society's *Geographical Journal* kept people informed of progress. The King expressed interest in having seeds sent to Windsor, and Kingdon Ward in distant China captured the mood: 'The Everest Expedition is "frightfully exciting" as school girls say.'[4] On 7 November anticipation increased as the President of the RGS stated triumphantly, 'Mr. Wollaston has made valuable and interesting collections of the plants, birds, animals and insects.'[5] A month later the Daily Mail reported that 'The height record of the world was won by a tiny plant … from 20,400 feet [6200 m].'

Heavy snow storms slowed seed collection in October, but Wollaston was pleased with his haul and wired that boxes of birds, mammals and dried plants should arrive around 25 November. They should be opened without delay because one of them contained seeds. Ironically, the collections were held up in the Thames by a fog, but they were delivered on 1 December and the seeds and dried plants were taken to Kew, where Sir David Prain shared out the seeds. Everything was in beautiful condition.

There were about 130 different packets of seed,[6] and Bulley was sent a share of nearly everything. They arrived by registered post. Bulley's enterprise and generosity were acknowledged by the secretary of the RGS, Mr Arthur R Hinks, who hoped for a repeat subscription in 1922. He received the terse reply, 'I will decide about another subscription when I have seen what this one produces.'[7]

He was to learn that the expedition found the high alpine slopes carpeted with ten different species of gentian and a dozen species of saxifrage, with primulas in special abundance. There were 18 species of primula, sometimes filling the air with their scent. Many of the species had been found before in Sikkim, but there were two new species. One was named after the leader of the expedition, Col Howard-Bury (*Primula buryana*) and the other in honour of the naturalist, Dr A F R Wollaston (*P. wollastonii*) (see Plate 28). They became known as the 'Mt Everest primulas'. Wollaston discovered them at about 4500 m in the Rongshar valley, after stumbling over glaciers and moraines in impenetrable fog. 'Our views of the mountains were none at all, but the beauty of the flowers at our feet were almost compensation for that.' One particularly caught his eye, and he described it vividly: 'It carried from 4 to 6 bells, each as big as a lady's thimble, of deep azure blue and lined inside with frosted silver.'[8] He asked if his name could be given to this 'heavenly flower' and it was agreed to 'immortalise him as he desires'.[9]

The Mount Everest reconnaissance team, 1921. Standing (left to right): Wollaston, Howard-Bury, Heron, Raeburn. Sitting: Mallory, Wheeler, Bullock, Morshead.

Primula wollastonii is unique to Everest and the Nepal – Tibet border, where it has a very restricted range, growing on sheltered mossy slopes covered by snow for six months of the year. Its discovery in 1921 vindicated Bulley's desire to fund plant collection on Everest. But it did not flower in Britain until seed was gathered in 1930. *Primula buryana* is a beautiful little plant, similar to *P. eburnea* (Plate 27), Cooper's 'gem' of nearby Bhutan. And because the Everest Expedition ventured on slopes within Nepal, this primula was discovered earlier than most Nepalese species of that then 'forbidden kingdom'.

Wollaston, like Bulley, cherished the hope that many of the plants would 'live in the gardens of this country.' But unfortunately his two new primulas are in the Soldanelloides group of high-altitude primulas similar to those Cooper found in Bhutan. It is very difficult to reproduce the best growing conditions for them in this country, but those who succeed are rewarded by the most exquisitely delicate flowers.

A second try and disaster

Satisfied that at least the expedition had found some new primulas, Bulley sent £100 for the second, 1922, expedition. Mr Hinks, Secretary of the RGS, acknowledged Bulley's 'kind contribution' and hoped there would be even more seed this time. As a non-botanist, he also asked for Bulley's guidance because 'The Horticultural Society thought that last year they [the expedition] devoted themselves too exclusively to rarities.' Bulley's hackles rose. He let fling with anger and contempt:[10]

> Dear Mr Hinks
>
> If the Mt. E. expedition collectors are going to devote themselves to 'hardy strains of common spp. for breeding' or any similar tosh, please cancel my cheque. What on earth do the idiots mean? The present strains of the common spp. are amply hardy. I grow lots of them here year after year …
>
> The Mt. E. expedition gives an opportunity of getting into cultivation beautiful hardy wild flowers which are not yet in the Gardens of the World. And it is to aid that excellent cause that I subscribe.
>
> A K Bulley

He was assured that the expedition would still do its best to get new things, too. Bulley let them keep his money.

However, Bulley became anxious at the low germination rate of the 1921 seeds from Everest. 'Here some Meconopsids have germinated, and a few other things. But not a single Primula or Gentian has yet shown up. And this is all the more striking because … seeds collected for me in China, by Kingdon Ward, are germinating like turf.'[11]

Nil desperandum being a good motto for seed growers as well as mountaineers, he thought round ways to improve seed germination next time. He wrote to Mr Hinks:

> It would be sad indeed if any results of this unique expedition should be lost, when they might perhaps have been saved. And therefore I am going to risk your considering me very impertinent by emphasising what I have found the essential thing in sending home 'hardy' seeds which have to pass through the tropics.[12]

He made two recommendations. Firstly he suggested that the seeds should be dried very thoroughly by sun or by the heat of a fire: 'Reggie Farrer, when plagued by perpetual cloud and rain, used fire heat with excellent success. If this is not done, the seeds "sweat" on their way home, and lose their vitality.'

Secondly he recommended a 'dodge' which both Cooper and Ward had tried, in packing the seeds in air which had extra carbon dioxide in it. 'CO_2 can be got easily from the "sparklets" which are used everywhere in the East for imparting fizz to drinks.' Ward had packed the seeds in small envelopes and placed them in a deep and narrow tin with a well-fitting lid, such as a Kodak film tin. The compressed air and carbon dioxide in a siphon were then allowed to flow gently into the tin and the lid soldered on. Bulley was thrilled with the results. 'This year Ward sent me in CO_2 a small portion of his finest things, including gentians and primulas, and 75% of them have already germinated.' Mr Hinks expressed interest, and asked to see one of the tins that Ward used. Sadly, however, events eclipsed such finesse of seed treatment.

The expedition set off expectantly from London; it was the best-equipped expedition ever sent to the Himalayas. For the botanical work there was a flora to study on the way out and a pamphlet of 'Hints for collectors'. There was to be a full-blown effort to reach the summit, and the initial stages went well, setting up three low camps, a fourth on the North Col and a fifth higher up the ridge to the summit. But the third attempt on the summit ended in tragedy. On 7 June the breaking monsoon started a snow storm lasting 36 hours. An avalanche swept across the slope leading to the North Col and killed seven of the porters.[13] It was the most serious disaster that had ever befallen a British mountain party, and the end of their attempt on the mountain peak. Within six weeks of establishing the base camp most of the best climbers were frostbitten, too, and an exhausted party came down the mountain without being able to make full use of the summer. A report of the expedition said that they sent to England some samples of agricultural seeds … and it is maybe as well there is no record of Bulley's verbal reaction! A 1922 report from Wisley reads: 'The seeds obtained as a result of the two Mt Everest expeditions are very scanty and at present not very promising.' Bulley did not try again.

Ward victorious in south-east Tibet

It was Ward who turned up trumps after the Everest fiasco. Finds from his 1921 expedition to Muli, China, included a new gentian which was named after Bulley's head gardener, *Gentiana hopei* (now *G. trichotoma*) (Plate 21) and won an award at Chelsea when shown by Bees in 1923. Flushed with this success, Ward asked Bulley if he would sponsor him for his next venture.[14] A syndicate was being organised by two bankers who were also keen gardeners, Frederick Stern of Highdown, Sussex, and Lionel de Rothschild of Exbury. Ward was to cross the Himalayas by the Everest expedition route but then turn east, in Tibet, to the upper Tsangpo valley and gorges. A Major F M Bailey, whom they both admired, had previously explored part of the gorge and he had even found a blue poppy, *Meconopsis baileyi*, which had never been found since! There were still unexplored stretches of the gorge and maybe the poppy would be there.

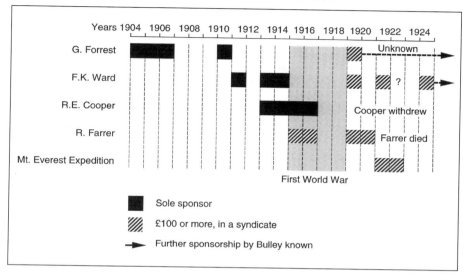

Twenty years of plant hunting in the Sino-Himalaya, sponsored by A K Bulley / Bees Ltd.

Ward's zest for the unknown, for those blank spaces on the map, were rather too familiar to Bulley from their early days. But now Ward was more experienced, and his enquiring, academic mind was fascinated by possible geographical links between the floras of China and the Himalayas, especially for primulas. He wanted to test his theories, which meant that his plant collecting had to be thorough. Furthermore, it emerged that Ward would have with him a young energetic companion, Lord Cawdor, who would do the surveying to give Ward more opportunities for plant and seed collection. Bulley took his chance and promised £150 in return for a share of the seeds.[15]

Ward botanised for about six months, hunting for plants in the Tsangpo valley and the ranges to the north and south of it. He reported that the 'rhododendrons and primulas here are simply astounding.' By August Ward reported finding nearly 50 species of rhododendron, about 40 primulas and 10 poppies … and this included the same species of poppy as Bailey had found![16]

Ward and Cawdor bivouacked in storms and dug plants out of the snow for their seeds. Seeds were packed and sent to the sponsors in February 1925 and the following year some of the treasures were proudly exhibited. Bulley showed a charming primula named after Cawdor, *P. cawdoriana*. It was later illustrated in *Curtis's Botanical Magazine* where it was reported that Bulley's 'very fine specimens' received an award of merit at a meeting of the RHS in May 1926.[17] *Primula florindae*, named after Ward's wife, Florence, also received an award of merit, and has become very popular in gardens, including Ness (see Plate 12).

But the sensation of the summer was *Meconopsis baileyi* (now called *M. betonicifolia*) (Plate 24). Ward had obtained exact details as to where Bailey had found his blue poppy. He visited the same spot at the same time of year and was thrilled to find it growing in great profusion on the banks of the Tsangpo. Moreover, he collected a pound of seed, from which the whole European stock is said to have been derived. This superb blue poppy gained an award of merit when Lady Aberconway and the Hon. H D McLaren of Bodnant showed it at Chelsea. In 1927 a plant could sell for a guinea, but among the first people to admire its flowers at Ness Gardens must have been the families of striking miners who came for a stroll on a Sunday afternoon. By 1929 a large bed of it flowered magnificently in Kensington Gardens. Today it is still cherished, its sky-blue flowers about 8 cm across, invariably making you stop in your tracks, just as Ward did when he found it in its Tibetan home.

Bulley had been proved right to persevere in supporting Ward despite Ward's shaky beginnings in plant collecting. After 15 years' experience Ward was able to state in 1926, 'To collect seeds of beautiful hardy plants for English gardens. That is my profession.'[18] It had not seemed so clear in earlier years, and Bulley had harboured many doubts. But now it was clear that they shared the same fundamental aims.

Ward found it easier to obtain funds after the success of the 1924 expedition. And Bulley was happy to play a minor role, although he received

Arisaema candidissimum, collected by Forrest and Ward, and shown by Bulley at Chelsea in 1924.

samples of Ward's seeds until the early 1930s. He continued to concentrate on growing seeds of alpine and hardy herbaceous plants, while other syndicate members, such as Lionel de Rothschild, specialised in rhododendrons. However, when Bulley received inappropriate seed from Ward in 1931 (probably seeds of half-hardy plants from Burma) his forthright reply might have offended anyone who did not know him. His handwriting was shaky, but his message was crisp and clear: 'Ward seeds recd.; n.b.g. for me'![19]

'Adieu, L. hancockianum!'

Threading through all these years of hunting in the Sino-Himalaya, there was the occasional idiosyncratic search for a particular plant. One of these, *Lithospermum hancockianum* (syn. *Arnebia hockianum*), outshone the others in the fun it gave both Balfour and Bulley. And in retirement, after the dramas of Everest, Bulley hoped he would find it at last. He wrote in 1926, 'I am carrying on a desperate struggle to get seed.' He imagined that the plant would have beautiful blue flowers – his favourite colour – and he had hunted for it for over a decade.

This flower had only been reported from one limestone crag in Yunnan in 1894! How could seed be retrieved? Discussion with Balfour began in 1911, and Balfour sent a herbarium sample to Père Edouard-Ernest Maire, who was then Pro-Vicar Apostolic of Yunnan province. Appended was the message, 'a sample of plant of which seed wanted.' Success ensued, Balfour and Bulley shared the seed, but the plants died without flowering. Then three different routes to the treasure were tried. First, another sample of a dried specimen was sent to a friend of Forrest. Second, Ward was instructed to look out for it. Third, Bulley provided a £5 cheque to bribe Père Maire to gather another lot of seed! All without avail.

Any other person might have given up, but in 1926 Bulley tried a last tack. He wrote to Augustine Henry to see if he could think back to his collecting days in Yunnan. Could he advise on the likely spot? But Henry could not help. Bulley acknowledged defeat in happy mood, being in San Francisco on a world tour at the time. 'From this time forth I renounce, denounce and abandon the wretched thing ...'[20] He had learned that the flowers were lilac and not blue, and not likely to be hardy.

> So adieu, L. *hancockianum*! I once had you from seed ... And I should well like to see you, just because I've hunted for you for so many years. But none the less you are a fraud. And as my job is the getting into cultivation of beautiful hardy plants, I will return with redoubled ardour towards other charmers – *Myosotis capitata* on Auckland Island; *Fritillaria nobilis* near Lake Vancouver; *Gypsophila vascifolia* from the Lebanon ... it's a proper fag. But one gets compensation when one bags a desideratum.

And he carried on round the world.

Part III

The Wide-ranging Enthusiast

9

Snowdon: Conflict with Conservationists

Making Snowdon Blossom (The Observer 16 October 1921)

An alpine garden on Snowdon?

In his ardour Bulley extended his ideas. As well as introducing beautiful plants into people's gardens, he thought it would be interesting to grow some in a more 'natural' montane setting. It would be a valid ecological experiment, and if successful, then walkers would come upon them with delight, adding further joy to the mountain scenery.

The idea of creating alpine gardens began in the Swiss Alps in the 1880s and by the turn of the century there was a movement in Europe to create gardens of alpine plants on the mountains. They were used to experiment with plant growth under different conditions of climate and soils, to conserve native species which were being dug up and removed, and to display and popularise their beauty. They were not all restricted to native plants, either, for in 1889, at Bourg St Pierre, Valais, the keen Swiss, Henri Correvon, created a garden with alpine plants from all over the world, including the Himalayas. He claimed it was a complete success, and as other alpine gardens were starting in the Alps and the Vosges, he wrote in an English journal, in 1905, encouraging the same in Britain. He described a large garden of 14–15 acres (5–6 ha), on the spur of a mountain, where about 30 'rockeries' of various sizes were scattered along a path winding down from the summit for some 500 feet (150 m). He said: 'The plants represent every quarter and almost every mountain region of the globe.'[1] Well! Bulley was keen to start an alpine garden in Britain. He decided to contact the directors of the botanic gardens.

In October 1915 Bulley wrote to Professor Bayley Balfour in Edinburgh:

> I have often thought it would be a nice thing to buy a Scottish and/or English mountain, and hand it to you or Kew, and see how far you could naturalise the beautiful shrubs, herbaceous [plants] and alpines of the temperate world on it. The difficulties are of course such things as heather, long grass, grazing and absence of snow. Still *G. verna* [*Gentiana verna*] does all right in Teesdale. So perhaps it might be done. I wonder what a mountain with no shooting value costs …[2]

Balfour was greatly impressed by the idea. The study of ecology was in its early days and he welcomed Bulley's suggestion. Indeed, for years he had tried to persuade owners of mountain regions in Scotland to establish a garden for alpines. 'I am convinced that [it] ... would be one of the most interesting

experimental cultural areas ... the project of taking a mountain and systematically planting it with foreign alpine and herbaceous plants has not been attempted.'[3] He found the scheme invigorating. Only the wartime lack of young active gardeners prevented immediate action, but he promised to develop the idea when the war ended. Meanwhile he would study geological maps to help locate a promising area for the experiment.

Bulley was thrilled. His mountain garden in Scotland was to become, horticulturally, the most interesting spot in Great Britain, and a splendid encouragement for other people. He tentatively thought of spending about £5000 ...[4]

After the war, Bulley's enthusiasm grew. He was now very wealthy, so he had the means as well as the dreams for this new project. He took the idea to the directors of the botanic gardens at Glasnevin and Kew. To Sir David Prain at Kew he explained that, in addition to his Scottish project, he would be willing to purchase a piece of mountain land

A K Bulley, inveterate letter writer, at his desk in the drawing room, c. 1920.

somewhere in England or Wales, and to present it to Kew for the naturalisation of beautiful hardy plants.[5] Prain expressed interest, and the delighted Bulley said that he would be prepared to spend £1500–£2000, assuming the price of suitable land was about £1 per acre.[6]

Snowdon was Bulley's choice, because it is the highest mountain in England and Wales, and harbours many native alpine plants, so maybe it would provide the ideal conditions for alien alpines, too. He was advised that the north-facing corrie, Cwm Glas, would be the best place. It has relatively long-lying snow in winter, locally rich soils on limestone outcrops, and steep, north-facing cliffs. Furthermore, Bulley lived only a car ride away and there were advantages in using the narrow-gauge Snowdon Mountain Railway from Llanberis to carry the plants and other paraphernalia up the mountain. This railway was opened in 1896, and ascends the north-west slopes of Snowdon, passing near the top of Cwm Glas.

Cwm Glas was then part of the Vaynol estate, and Bulley began negotiations with the trustees. They declined to allow Bulley to purchase, but offered him a lease of 500 acres (200 ha) at a nominal rent, to plant alpines as he wished, in the open ground or in enclosures. The 'go-ahead' had been given! Bulley was very excited and wrote to Prain, 'What fun if we presently found out that some of the fine European and Asiatic alpines could hold their own under our conditions!'[7]

Professor Farmer, an expert on Snowdonia, recommended initial planting on a terrace at the head of Cwm Glas. It was remote from any track and likely to be visited only by botanists or alpine climbers whom they trusted would not tamper with plants, and the experimental plot was only to be 30 yards x 10 yards (27 m x 9 m), the size of a moderate suburban garden. Enclosure from the ravages of tourists and sheep was discussed but rejected, at least for the first winter. Bulley could see no need to bar the sheep. 'Sheep will keep the grass short. They are all over the Alps and don't seem to affect the display of flowers. I suppose they prefer grass. There's no accounting for taste.'[8] As a precaution against vandalism, it was agreed that an informative noticeboard should be erected at the entrance to the terrace, as long as it was inconspicuous at a distance, so as not to attract attention. Bulley proposed the following wording:

> The Director of Kew is carrying out on this terrace an interesting experiment. Its object is to ascertain whether alpine plants from all parts of the world will grow on Snowdon. The public are earnestly invited to cooperate by refraining from touching the plants. They will thereby make it possible to leave the area open.[9]

Bulley listed possible plants which he had growing in his struck cuttings house and rockery, and sent the list to Kew for approval. A foreman from Kew, Mr W Irving, was to bring other plants and seeds with him, for this was a joint expedition. Bulley offered transport and labour, including a photographer, a signboard man, and others to carry the plants and tools.

A date was set for September 1921, as the best time for moving plants before the railway closed for the winter. Sir David and Lady Prain were invited

Part of the experimental plot on Snowdon, including the noticeboard and numbered plants. These included Primula rosea (79) from the north-west Himalayas, and Codonopsis bulleyana (83) from Yunnan, China.

for the planting, and when the time came, on 24 September 1921, the plot of land was successfully planted with 88 different kinds of alpine species, all of which were listed, numbered and photographed.

It was a cosmopolitan collection. Our native yellow mountain saxifrage, *Saxifraga aizoides*, and rock plants from the Alps, such as the alpine snowbell, *Soldanella alpina*, and *Androsace carnea*, shared the plot with others from afar. There were *Androsace lanuginosa*, *Mertensia primuloides* and *Primula rosea* from the Himalayas, *Astilbe simplicifolia* from Japan and *Acaena buchananii* from the South Island of New Zealand. Some were introduced by Bulley's collectors: George Forrest's elegant *Primula vialii* (Plate 9) and *Codonopsis bulleyana*, and Reginald Farrer's spectacular *Gentiana farreri* (Plate 23). There were no rhododendrons. Some of the plants are easy to grow in gardens, like the Italian *Campanula garganica*, whilst others are best suited to a trough, like *Dianthus microlepis*. No one knew how they would stand up to the plant competition or the weather on Snowdon, or what effect the sheep and other two- and four-footed depredators would have. It was a test of survival.[10]

But within three weeks the press had heard of their scheme and exaggerated its scale and content, so that Bulley's experiment was blown up into a really good story. A stunned Bulley wrote hastily to Prain: 'I write in great irritation. There is in today's *Daily Mail* [17 October 1921] a notice about the Snowdon planting. The wretches rang me up last night. I need hardly say that the statement in the last par. is wholly imagining. Beastly sensationalists!'[11] The report to which he referred said that a large tract of land had been planted, that in a few years a greater part of Snowdon would be covered with alpine flowers, and that Chinese rhododendrons were to be planted in the spring. The *Evening News* (19 October 1921) had a similar story. Poor Bulley! He had not thought that the noticeboard would lead to this. His small-scale, private scheme had become maddeningly public and grossly misrepresented.

The *Observer* (16 October 1921) prophesied, 'All being well, there will, within the next three or four years, be large sweeps of alpine flowers blossoming on Snowdon with a freedom rivalling their native home.' Such dreaming sparked controversy. It was followed by a reader's letter (23 October 1921) pointing out that the experiment might be welcome to rock gardeners, but not to those who loved the distinctive character of Snowdon and its native flora. He also added another twist: 'Would it not be much wiser to give protection to our diminishing mountain flowers …?'

What could Bulley do? He discussed it with Prain, who put an explanatory, matter-of-fact notice in the next issue of the *Kew Bulletin*,[12] saying that it was a desirable experiment, done in consultation with the director of Kew, the advice of Professor Farmer and the permission of the Vaynol trustees. They hoped that the furore would calm down although Bulley's worst fears were expressed in his joke that the press story would be in the guide books the next year. However, Bulley remained positive and was looking ahead to the following spring! He wrote to Prain, 'I shall try to meet Prof. Farmer on the spot, and shall if poss. take with me Prof. Boswell [Percy G H Boswell], the Geologist of

(Right) The Snowdon experiment was exaggerated by the press, and provoked correspondence in several newspapers.

From The General Press Cutting Association, Ltd
ATLANTIC HOUSE,
45-50, HOLBORN VIADUCT, E.C. 1.
TELEPHONE: HOLBORN 4815.

Cutting from the _Evening News_

Address of Publication

Issue dated 19 . 10 . 21

KEW BULBS FOR SNOWDON.
Director and Alpine Plant Expert Make an Interesting Experiment.

A large tract of land on the Llanberis, Carnarvonshire, side of Mount Snowdon has been planted with Alpine plants and seeds taken from Alpine flowers in Kew Gardens.

The director of Kew, Sir David Prain, with Mr. Walter Irving, a Kew Alpine expert, and Mr. T. R. Bulley, recently visited the spot and spent a week-end on the planting.

"The experiment," said Mr. Bulley, " is to be continued every year until the greater part of Snowdon is covered with Alpine flowers.

"It is to be hoped that tourists will help us by not tampering with them."

Chinese rhododendrons are to be planted on the slopes of Snowdon next spring.

315

From The General Press Cutting Association, Ltd
ATLANTIC HOUSE,
45-50, HOLBORN VIADUCT, E.C. 1.
TELEPHONE: HOLBORN 4815.

Cutting from the _Observer_

Address of Publication

Issue dated 23 . 10 . 21

SNOWDON-CUM-KEW.

Sir,—Your announcement that the Llanberis side of Snowdon, a locality rich in British mountain plants, including such "alpines" as the meadow rue, globe flower, rock cress, moss campion, saussurea, spiderwort, rose-root, and several species of saxifrages, is now being sown by Kew specialists with seeds of various Swiss flowers, with Chinese rhododendrons to follow, will be more gratefully received by rock-gardeners than by those lovers of the wild who have a regard for the distinctive character of Snowdon itself, and for its native flora.

Would it not be much wiser to give protection to our own diminishing mountain flowers than to introduce a host of aliens? There could be no objection to the reintroduction of certain rare natives—the clustered saxifrage, for example—which have become exceedingly scarce during the past fifty years, owing in part to the depredations of collectors; but the wholesale sowing and planting of foreign species seems quite uncalled for.

A country which has allowed its finest mountain to be exploited for commercial purposes by the building of a railway and "summit hotel," is perhaps hardly in a position to protest against a Welsh hillside being planted with Chinese rhododendrons; but such schemes are none the less incongruous and barbaric, and raise the question: What sort of mountain do we desire to have? A piece of nature, or a nursery garden? A Snowdon, or a Snowdon-cum-Kew?

Yours faithfully,
HENRY S. SALT.
19, Highdown-road, Brighton.

314

From The General Press Cutting Association, Ltd
ATLANTIC HOUSE,
45-50, HOLBORN VIADUCT, E.C. 1.
TELEPHONE: HOLBORN 4815.

Cutting from the _Glasgow Bulletin_

Address of Publication

Issue dated 2 . 1 . 12 . 21

Upsetting Nature!

The proposed "Alpine Garden" on Snowdon, even though it appears to be under the auspices of Kew, by no means has the approval of all interested in Alpine plants. In fact the members of the Natural History Society of Glasgow, which contains numerous ardent lovers of the mountain flora and which every year has an "Alpine" excursion to the Highlands, have just entered a protest against the scheme. People who study the wild native plants—and animals, too—object to the upsetting of nature by the introduction of aliens, however beautiful. A move was on foot this year to have a similar garden in the Forfarshire hills, but

Liverpool University. My notion is to make the next planting a good deal higher up. What are your views?'[13]

However, despite his wish to continue with the experiment, Bulley became deeply concerned for the implications of Kew's involvement. For himself he 'did not care a cuss', but he wrote very apologetically to the director, regretting that his own misguided enthusiasm had put Prain in an embarrassing position. He would willingly give up mountain plantings rather than draw upon Kew any antagonistic feeling. He could justify his scheme to himself, but he could see that he could not convince people who, as he thought, were reacting with prejudice and sentiment. He realised that a general acceptance by the public was necessary for the continuance of the scheme. 'I think now that the choice of Snowdon was a mistake. It is, very properly, a centre of sentiment. I was blinded by its suitability.'[14] It was decided to leave the experiment for nine months, and Bulley would watch what happened to the plants during the summer.

Bulley's instinct was to turn to the proposed Scottish project with renewed vigour. But here Bulley was in another dilemma. Balfour was forced to resign from his position in Edinburgh because of broken health. Bulley wrote him a sensitive and sympathetic letter, but on the alpine garden in Scotland he did not know what to say:

> On the one hand I know that it would be a great pleasure to you to put it through, on the other hand I know that extra worry is just the very last thing you ought to undertake. I cannot express any opinion on this matter. It must lie with Lady Balfour, and with your medical man.[15]

However, Balfour, after investigating one area which was too expensive at £15 000, was in the middle of correspondence with Lord Airlie about the possibility of an alpine garden in the Caenlochan Deer Forest, which he considered an ideal spot. He encouraged Bulley to go on with his experiment, reporting that Lord Airlie was really bitten by the proposal, but unfortunately Balfour died in 1922, before negotiations were completed. The Caenlochan alpine garden never materialised. Prain also retired from Kew the same year. It was as if the alpine garden projects began like one great catherine wheel of whirring excitement, but several deluges of water were causing them to splutter and die out. By 1925 the noticeboard on Snowdon was lying on the screes below, and there were very few plants growing on the terrace. It may have been that the summers were too cool and short for the plants to ripen seed, and many, especially the primulas, are relatively short-lived in the wild.

The Snowdon saga, however, resurfaced ten years later. Despite his former feelings that the choice of Snowdon was a mistake, Bulley maintained his lease in Cwm Glas. He was his father's son, and if either of them got their teeth into something, they wouldn't let go! Enthusiasm for rock gardens and alpine plants was growing in Britain. Bulley bided his time. Then the newly formed Alpine Garden Society arranged a week's autumn holiday for members 'in conjunction with the Management of the Snowdon Mountain Railway and the Royal Victoria Hotel, Llanberis, from October 1st–8th 1932.' Bulley, aged 72, grasped his opportunity to offer the society further experiments in Cwm Glas. No decision was taken then, but he invited members to visit the Cwm. A quantity of seed of Asiatic alpine primulas and other plants was quietly broadcast at a height of some 850 m on the slopes beneath the Clogwyn station of the Snowdon mountain railway![16]

Again, Bulley's offer was leaked to the papers, and he must have been stunned by the strong, adverse, public reaction. *The Times* even had a leading article on the subject (28 October 1932). Probably worse still, to Bulley, the Linnean Society – the oldest body in the country exclusively devoted to natural history – took a very serious view: its Council was unanimous in objecting to the scheme, and its President wrote to *The Times* (28 October 1932) while the Council 'resolved to ask the President [Professor F E Weiss FRS] to bring the matter before the Committee of the Plant Conservation Board.'[17] The President of the Linnean Society suggested that the Vaynol estate would be better used for a sanctuary for rare British plants.

Bulley's last spark of hope for this project was extinguished.

Bulley's clash with conservation

By experimenting with exotics on Snowdon, Bulley was putting his hand in a hornets' nest. He got stung, and when he tried again, the sting was worse. From today's viewpoint it is surprising that he ever tried, but at that time the conservation movement was embryonic. His interests had moved away from natural history to horticulture and plant introductions. A possible threat to the fragile future of the native arctic-alpine vegetation was not in his sights! Any complication on the mountain signalled danger to conservationists; experiments on the growth and introduction of other alpine plants seemed progressive to Bulley. There was an inherent conflict.

In defence of Bulley, he was pioneering in Britain the kind of scheme which had been very successful in the European Alps. Many people flocked to see those alpine gardens. There, Bulley had seen introduced plants growing side by side with native alpines on the rocky slopes. Moreover, if an introduced plant naturalised locally it was reported with interest rather than anger; it was not perceived as a threat. When the lady's slipper orchid (*Cypripedium calceolus*) spread into the surrounding grassland, at Bourg St Pierre, Valais, someone wrote with pleasure, that it grew 'as if it had been there for all time.'[18] That is the kind of response which Bulley had hoped for, if someone found *Gentiana farreri* (Plate 23) on Snowdon!

Bulley was not warned or advised against his scheme by the eminent botanists he consulted. He sought the advice of Professor J B Farmer, who had written the only contemporary, comprehensive account of the flora on Snowdon, and it was he who advised Bulley to plant in Cwm Glas, botanically the finest cwm of Snowdon. Bulley also had the backing of two directors of royal botanic gardens, Prain and Balfour, and when the first storm broke,

Balfour wrote sympathetically: 'It must be disillusioning to have your efforts at benefitting your fellowmen received as they are, and criticised.' He pointed out that the Forestry Commission was already 'changing the plant denizens.'[19]

Bulley had no expectation of the introduced plants spreading all over the mountain. That his introduced plants would cause any rare native alpine to be exterminated, was probably laughable to him. Garden escapees often don't last long, and they are rarely invasive in established communities. If naturalisation had taken place, to Bulley that would have been a bonus, adding beauty to the mountain! But he realised that the likelihood was that they would die out, either being smothered in grasses, or eaten by sheep or mountain slugs. But a monitored experiment seemed to him a reasonable, scientific thing to try. Indeed, in defence of Bulley, Sir William Lawrence wrote to *The Times* (16 October 1932) pointing out that it was very difficult to cultivate alpines in the open, and that it would be 'impossible to naturalize them'. He did not even rule out further experiments: 'The most that might be done by the Alpine Garden Society on Snowdon would be to fence an acre against sheep with a view to trying out foreign species under Alpine conditions.' So Bulley had eminent allies in the gardening world.

The clash was fundamentally between horticulturalists who were used to introducing and experimenting with exotics, and naturalists who had a purist, protectionist approach to the indigenous flora, and feared that the introduced plants might interbreed with the native plants, bring new pests with them, or even oust rare plants which lacked competitive vigour because they were on the margin of their range.

Codonopsis bulleyana *has exquisite pale blue flowers.*

Unfortunately for Bulley, too, he had not realised the news value of his scheme. After all, it was a novel idea for a famous mountain in Britain: Chinese plants 'blossoming on Snowdon' catches the imagination, with all the evocation of flowers from the exotic East. It was also controversial. The romance of Chinese plants on a British mountain was countered by feelings of sentimental attachment to the present landscapes and flowers of Snowdon. It was also threatening: Snowdon was 'sacred' to botanists who were anxious to defend its ancient arctic-alpine flora. At the time, 64 flowering plants and ferns on Snowdon were listed as arctic-alpine in distribution, some of them petering out at the southern limit of their range, and only present on Snowdon in very small patches. Already, the unique assemblage of alpine plants on Snowdon had been vandalised, some plants hovering on the verge of extinction. The fern flora succumbed to a major fad for ferns in the 1840s and 1850s. At the summit of Snowdon in 1849, visitors were greeted by local dealers hawking Holly ferns at sixpence a root! When, from the end of the last century, the mountain railway took people to the top of Snowdon, the threat to the fragility of soils and flowers was increased. It made Bulley's experiment easier to carry out, but it is no wonder botanists were anxious. Time has shown that they had good reason. By 1966 it was stated that the holly fern, *Polystichum lonchitis*, in Cwm Glas, was ten times harder to find than it probably would have been in the seventeenth century;[20] the royal fern, *Osmunda regalis*, was nearly exterminated, and the two woodsias, *Woodsia ilvensis* and *W. alpina*, were extremely rare.

The background of depredation of the flora over a long period of time, including the effects of other human activities, such as quarrying, increased botanists' sensitivity to further interference. Besides, *The Times* leading article (28 October 1932) pointed out that there was no need to 'take all that trouble at 3,000 feet up, because these Alpine things could be grown perfectly well at sea level'! However, Bulley's deed was done. Kew began to dissociate itself from the project, after the first round of attacks, and a writer in the *Bulletin of the Alpine Garden Society*, 1933, summed up the current feeling: 'Any introduction of alien species would be an entirely new factor which may produce unforeseen disturbances ... It must be our privilege to guard these treasures [the native alpine plants] from all unwarrantable interference ...'[21]

That was in 1933, when there was increased interest in nature conservation. If Bulley had tried his experiment before or during the First World War, he would probably have got away with it! The fracas with Bulley indicates the level of increasing concern, although the first nature reserve in Snowdonia was not designated until 1954.

But nature reserves don't solve all problems. Since Bulley's day, the fear of rhododendrons on the mountain has been justified. Nearly 60 years after Bulley's débâcle on Snowdon, *The Independent* newspaper had the following scary headline: 'Rhododendrons introduced as ornamental shrubs could soon wreck Snowdonia' (4 June 1990). This has nothing to do with Bulley, and does not concern the alpine areas, but it shows that fears of invasion by rhododendrons were understandable. The only rhododendrons that Bulley contemplated for Snowdon were *R. intricatum* and *R. impeditum*, both of which were from China. In fact, Bulley did not plant any. The present creeping scourge is *R. ponticum*, introduced more than 200 years ago from Turkey and the Iberian peninsula.

The final irony is that during his life, Bulley showed early awareness of the need to protect wildlife and landscape. He gave moorland and woodland to the National Trust. But in keeping with his socialist ideals, through the Footpaths and Open Spaces Preservation Society, he also fought for 'the right of everyone to have freedom of access to the land of their birth without fear of laws of trespass.' On Snowdon, access by many people, with conflicting aims and different perceptions, was beginning to create problems which have been with us ever since. This has led to the necessity for nature reserves, the allocation of areas of special scientific interest, and for public enquiries. Even then, rare plants, like birds' eggs, are taken illegally from guarded sites. Bulley's experience was a foreboding of the problems and complexities which were to come.

But Bulley was philosophical: if one idea did not work, he took up another. Life was too short to let things rankle. There were plenty of new possibilities to try out in his garden.

~ 10 ~

The Persevering Plantsman

Persevere: Look ahead: Be optimistic. It pays![1]

This is from a Bees' advertisement, and reflects Bulley's ebullience and outlook. He considered 'ennui' the scourge of the idle, and it never afflicted him.

A game with a serious purpose

Even while Bulley's main 'push' was for seed from the Sino-Himalaya, he was enlarging his plant collection from elsewhere. A man of restless energy, his letters skip from one topic to another, and likewise he could not focus entirely on seed of one area of the world. We have seen that he had his eye on Basutoland and New Guinea, the Karakorams and the Andes. If only he had more hours in the day, seven weeks in the month!

However, he had several decades! And when he established Bees Ltd and hired plant hunters, plant collecting became like a game of monopoly. Instead of buying and selling houses, he speculated on plants from different areas of the world. Some areas proved poor, others rich, and some he never 'stopped' on. His curiosity for the unknown, together with his love of plants, gave him a fillip, and he joked that life would be barren without it.

When introducing new plants through Bees Ltd, the stages Bulley went through were as follows:

1 Think of an area. Think of a group of plants you would like to try and grow. Find a good man willing to hunt for seeds.

2 Can you afford the cost?

   If YES, carry on. If NO, go back to the beginning.

3 Wait for the seeds to be sent to you. On arrival, share them with a botanic garden(s).

4 Experiment, and grow the plants if you can. (If the plant is new to science, collect a bonus – a plant is named after you, your nursery or your head gardener.)

5 Do any plants look promising as garden flowers?

If YES, propagate, exhibit, gain an award as bonus, carry on.

If NO, reject, lose money, go back to the beginning.

6 Will you sell now?

If YES, hope for your profit.

If NO, try your gardening skills, name new varieties or hybrids after Bees, hope for profits later!

The length of time this took varied enormously. Early successes with George Forrest's seeds took four to five years from stage 1 to stage 5 (gaining an award) for *Primula malacoides* and *P. bulleyana* (Plate 11). But sometimes it took at least two expeditions to get viable seed, or the seed would not germinate first time. For an award for *Roscoea humeana* (Plate 19), it took 16 years from stage 1 to stage 5.

Bulley lived at an ideal time to play this game. There were so many unexplored areas of the world which might yield new garden plants. When Bulley was a boy of only nine years, William Robinson wrote a pioneering book, *Alpine Flowers for English Gardens* (1870). His list of 'choicest alpine flowers' shows an overwhelming concentration on alpine flowers from Europe east to the Caucasus and the Carpathian Mountains. The huge numbers of hardy plants in the mountains of the Sino-Himalaya were largely waiting to be discovered. The Andes were hardly explored, the heights of the Rockies were only beginning to be hunted for plants. The rush for gold came much sooner! No wonder that an enthusiast such as Bulley later took opportunities to search for new flowers from the Rockies, Andes and elsewhere.

However, Bulley had to adapt his game as circumstances changed. As Bees Ltd concentrated more on the mass market, during and after the First World War, more new plants were exhibited in the name of Bulley himself. They were no longer sold but all were shared. If he speculated alone on a plant hunter, it was for a few weeks, not months or years. Then as other wealthy gardeners began to organise plant-hunting expeditions, Bulley subscribed for seeds in syndicates, as he had done for Farrer. Expeditions gained a Pavlovian response: subscribe. And as he became the Grand Old Man of alpine gardening, more would-be plant hunters came to him for financial support. No longer did he have to make the first move. It was a less aggressive, more relaxed situation. He would pay a seed-share if he wished, exhibit if he felt inclined. Life was no longer in any way like a game of monopoly; he was giving to a good cause.

The Rocky Mountains

When William Robinson crossed the Rockies by train in 1870, it was as if a veil of ignorance was lifted. He stopped to search for alpines in the patchy November snow. He wondered at the beauty of alpine phloxes, and reflected that very few of them had been introduced to Britain. As for the genus *Eriogonum*, which has many weeds in America, he was pleasantly surprised to find an alpine plant which was 'quite a gem of a rock-plant'.

Similarly, many other people began to hunt for hardy plants in the Rockies, and by the close of the nineteenth century, masses of its high-altitude plants were arriving in Britain. Even so, the Rocky Mountains were incompletely explored by 1900; they were not thoroughly criss-crossed until the 1930s. Bulley was at his most active during this 30-year period. There was plenty of room for him to introduce and re-introduce plants which were very rare or completely new to British gardeners.

We know of three contacts that Bulley had in the Rockies. One was E O Warton, who obtained plants for him from New Mexico. Another was Professor Aven Nelson (1859–1952), who built up an important herbarium at the University of Wyoming. The third was Darwin M Andrews (1869–1938) who founded a nursery of Rocky Mountain plants at Boulder, North Colorado.[2] When Bulley was establishing a core of American plants for his nursery, he bought 500 plants from Andrews.[3]

Bees' first catalogue, in March 1905, shows a good stock of American plants, including 43 sorts of *Phlox* and 51 sorts of *Penstemon*, many of them selling for 9d or 1s a plant. But it also indicates that some popular alpine plants of today were difficult to obtain. The lovely small alpine, *Phlox douglasii*, and *Penstemon hartwegii*, were both so rare that Bees sold them for the high price of 2s 6d per plant. There was only one *Lewisia*, the beautiful *L. rediviva*. There were four species of *Eriogonum*, and they tended to be expensive, with *E. jamesii* costing 2s 6d. This showed a large shortfall from those available today, for there are now over 40 species of this large genus listed in the Alpine Garden Society's *Encyclopaedia of Alpines*.

It was the genus *Eriogonum*, the predominantly alpine American buckwheats, which proved a particularly alluring but difficult challenge for Bulley. Some species were well known, having been found by famous early-nineteenth-century plant collectors such as David Douglas and Thomas Nuttall. Other species were simply undiscovered, not easily available, or their horticultural potential was completely untested. In the wild they grew in the mountainous west of North America. Even today this genus is not often seen in British gardens. However, 75–80 years ago Bulley and his gardeners were experimenting with pans of species from different areas of the Rockies. There was always the possibility that they would find a 'winner' among the weeds! The eriogonums were never a main interest of Bulley; he turned to them as a happy sideline, rather as someone else might pick up their embroidery which was taking a long time to finish in their spare time.

Before the First World War, in 1912, when he was enamoured of many new plants coming from China, Bulley declared that two American eriogonums, *Eriogonum wrightii* and *E. ovalifolium purpureum*, were 'two of the most beautiful alpines in existence'.[4] Seed was hard to procure and the botanic garden in Edinburgh had neither species at that time, so Bulley obtained seed direct from America and supplied the botanic gardens of both Kew and Edinburgh.[5]

As war raged in Europe, Bulley's thoughts turned again to North American plants. In spring 1915, he was encouraged by success: '*E. ovalifolium* is going to bloom, to my great joy.'[6] Then, as his professional plant hunters in Asia joined the war, and Bees Ltd was forced to close its New and Rare Plants Department, he defeated war weariness with the fun of a little flutter on a collector in California. In 1916 and 1917 he hired the services of a man called Chandler to collect seeds for six weeks in the Yosemite Alps of the Sierra Nevada, California.[7,8] Bulley searched for a handbook on the flora of the Yosemite National Park, and he examined herbarium specimens to weigh up the possibilities of finding something good. He was aware of the risks of receiving 'a lot of well known things and rubbish', but Balfour assured him that there were plenty of choice things to be had. And the growth of these seeds gave him an extra, momentary 'lift' in the midst of war. He reported to Balfour in 1917:

> Perhaps the pride of the season was Chandler's *Eriogonum parishii*. About a dozen seeds germinated in a pan. The Eriogonums transplant badly. So I put the whole pan out. At first they were quite insignificant. But ... now they are a red mist of tiny flowers, which in some lights are most beautiful.[9]

Balfour shared in his delight, but it was difficult to get seed from the plants and he was left sighing, 'What a pity it is that so many of these Californian plants are annuals.' We do not hear of it in cultivation today, and many other species of this genus are difficult to establish in British gardens.

However, it seems as if his family motto was ringing in his ears, because after the war Bulley could not let go of the eriogonums without another try at *E. wrightii*. He had a good idea. He wrote to Dr Purpus, superintendent of the botanical gardens at Darmstadt in Germany, because his brother often hunted for flowers in the Rockies. Bulley asked about Arizona, but was advised that the chances of finding *E. wrightii* there were too slim to be worth the travel costs.[10] However, Bulley persevered in his enquiries and achieved success two years later with a collector in southern California. He wrote jubilantly, 'I enclose seed which I hope is true (and good) of the long desired and glorious *Eriogonum wrightii* var. *subscaposum* – from 9000 feet [2743 m] altitude, San Bernardino Mountains.'[11] What triumph! Seed was sent to Kew and Bulley's handwritten note was glued into Kew's Inwards Book, permanently recording his great delight at his successful mission. Now that seed is more easily obtained from the Rockies, it is one of the buckwheats which is becoming more popular, as it grows quite quickly in an alpine house and even self-sows in the rock garden.

Bulley's perseverance with the eriogonums had a happy ending. But even if he had never found *E. wrightii* again, he would have thought his search worth while. He enjoyed the treasure hunt in the Rockies, and was always ready to embark on another, somewhere else on the globe.

The southern hemisphere

At last, on retirement from the family cotton firm in 1922, Bulley had the freedom to travel afar on his own personal hunt for plants. First stop was Cape Town for a healthy dose of warm sunshine in the winter of 1923–4. Probably this warmth was appreciated all the more when news came in January that James Ramsay MacDonald had been appointed as Britain's first Labour Prime Minister, with five Fabians in his Cabinet.

The refreshment of this South African trip seems encapsulated in a commission he was given. He had been asked by an enthusiast to bring back seeds of 'the most beautiful flower in the world'. 'This is rather a tall order,' wrote Bulley. 'However, I aided in getting a little seed, and one seed has now germinated. The plant's name is *Impatiens flanagae*, and it grows only at Port St John, S.A. I say my prayers over the seedling every morning.'[12]

Howard Carter had the thrill of discovering the sarcophagus in the tomb of Tutankhamun that year, but Bulley knew pleasure in smaller things. In his last letter to his son, Bulley wrote that 'the object of life is satisfaction'. In this instance he derived satisfaction, happiness and humour from finding and growing a balsam which was unique to a river bank at the mouth of the St John's River, Natal.

Visiting New Zealand was a particular joy in the winter of 1927–8, and Bulley and his daughter Lois stayed there for over two months. Previously, Bulley had received seeds from Dr Leonard Cockayne, a well-known New Zealand botanist, and so he was familiar with some little-known New Zealand alpines such as *Fostera bidwillii*. He once described this plant as becoming a weed on his rock garden moraine at Ness, where 'New Zealanders are hobnobbing with a N. American'! One of New Zealand's glories, the magnificent *Ranunculus lyalli*, had fascinated him for nearly 30 years. He had experimented with it out of doors, and when he had it in peat and shade and it pushed up a flower spike, he reported the thrill to Balfour, because it is so difficult to grow.

He delighted in seeing New Zealand's alpine treasures in their natural setting, and intrigued at the same time that the flora had a preponderance of white flowers (78% of the mountain flora). With his love of the northern hemisphere's blue gentians, the southern hemisphere's white and cream gentians particularly intrigued him. He had grown the endemic 'shore gentian', *Gentiana saxosa*, as long ago as 1898, but seeing the wild one was another kind of treat. Before leaving, he tried to arrange for a selection of plants to be sent to Bees. And when he moved on to Australia perhaps the best alpine he personally collected was the rare *Helipterum albicans* (syn. *H. incanum*) from the summits of the Blue Mountains.[13] It has lovely white-woolly leaves and decorative, large, white, everlasting flowerheads. Lois Bulley recalls that 'he actually dug up some white flowers we found at the top of a mountain ... [They] were carefully packed into my little rucksack, and tenderly carried back to England, the ship taking them through the tropics in her medium fridge.'[14]

But Bulley does not seem to have visited Central or South America, although he had his eye on sending a plant hunter there before the First World War. At that time he wanted to get his hands on one plant which was first found in the crater of a volcano in Guatemala in the early nineteenth century (*Weldenia candida*). In about 1912, Bulley imported it, probably through a cotton salesman, and grew 12 precious plants, when 'the few plants grown in Britain were known and numbered'.[15] He was so delighted that he sent a plant to Kew, and the following year Kew purchased another from Bees. Bees proudly announced in its catalogue: 'This was one of the plants which helped us to secure the "Farrer Cup" for rare alpines in open competition.' And you had to pay 3s 6d or 5s for a plant in 1915, one of the most expensive hardy plants in the catalogue.

After this *coup*, no wonder Bulley wanted to send a plant hunter to South America. In the 1890s he had grown some beautiful flowers from there, *Alstroemeria* from Chile and the rare *Anemone decapetela* from Peru. So what other charmers lay in store in those mountains? He heard that one of the best grounds for new hardy plants would be the Andes of Ecuador, Peru and Bolivia. Bulley checked with his mentor in Edinburgh. The reply was extremely positive:

> And so you are nibbling at the Andes! I wonder you have not been there before now. For several years past I have been urging every nurseryman I met to send men to the high Andes for plants. They much prefer to content themselves with the lower grounds where they can get orchids and things like that. But the whole field of the top Andes is practically unknown horticulturally and there are some wonderful gems to be got ... There is lots of money to be made. I hope you won't let the idea drop and will arrange to send somebody there.[16]

Flowering gems! Profits! Of course Bulley would have a go. What a splendid new adventure that would be. He discussed it with J C Williams of Caerhays, Cornwall, who agreed to combine on a joint sponsorship of a plant hunter in South America, if it could be arranged. Bulley had heard of a possible plant hunter, so he wrote to the director of Kew for advice:[17]

> Ness,
> Neston,
> Cheshire
> July 15, '12
>
> Dear Sir David Prain,
>
> Perhaps 2 months ago, one of my Cotton Salesmen introduced to me a friend of his, Humphreys by name, who had been botanizing in Mexico ... I had some talk with him, and it revived an old desire of mine to send a collector after Andine alpines, in Peru, Ecuador, Bolivia, etc...

(Right) **Plate 26.**
*Prayer flags at the
summit of the Yale La
pass, Bhutan. Here Cooper
discovered the spectacular
purple gentian,
Gentiana urnula.*

(Below left) **Plate 27.**
*Primula eburnea.
This tiny gem, with
flowers at most 1 cm
across, was discovered
by Cooper near a glacial
lake in Bhutan.*

(Below right) **Plate 28.**
*Primula wollastonii
was discovered by
Wollaston on the 1921
Everest expedition to
which Bulley subscribed.*

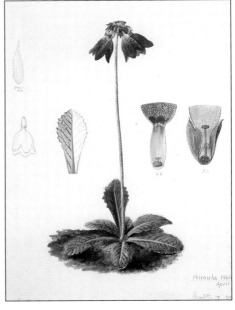

(Right) **Plate 29.** Viburnum grandiflorum, a sweet-scented, winter-flowering shrub raised from Cooper's Bhutan seed.

(Below) **Plate 30.** Rhododendron dalhousiae var. rhabdotum. Its showy flowers brought a thrill when discovered by Cooper in Bhutan.

(Facing page) **Plate 31.** Nomocharis aperta, a water colour by Farrer, capturing the character of the flower in the Burmese mountains, six weeks before he died there in 1920.

(Overleaf) **Plate 32.** 'Seeds that Grow' became Bees' famous slogan, and this 1926 catalogue cover emphasises Bees' trade in hardy herbaceous plant seeds.

Rhododendron rhabdotum
From Mrs Blathwayt, nest Porlock

I therefore write this line to say that I should be very much obliged, if you would let me know whether in your opinion Humphreys is a suitable person for such a job as the High Andes, and whether he would be likely to be open to an offer of the same kind as Forrest's – £200 and expenses.

I am,
Yours sincerely

A K Bulley

But the man was not available, and plant introduction from the Andes was postponed. A few years later Bulley was even discouraged by the keeper of the herbarium at Kew, Dr Stapf, who said there would be a lot of new species, but many in the hardy zone without garden value. 'Endless quantities of coarse composites and pigmy violas.' Then the First World War came …

However, ten years later, in 1925, he took his chance when it had become fashionable for wealthy gardeners to club together to finance expeditions. Within a few years he sponsored two plant hunters in the Andes. In 1925, the Hon. H D McLaren of Bodnant Gardens was arranging a syndicate with famous gardeners such as J C Williams and Lionel de Rothschild. Bulley joined them, subscribing a share in return for seeds.[18] The plant hunter was Harold Comber (1897–1969), who seemed to have had a love of flowers in his genes. His father was head gardener at Nymans, one of the beautiful Sussex gardens, and Harold was born in the head gardener's cottage there. He trained as a gardener, was familiar with many Andean plants, and longed to go plant hunting. On this expedition, Comber hunted in the high mountains west of Neuquen, in Argentina, because it was thought that this relatively unexplored area was the most likely to yield a large number of new, hardy plants. Comber's letters were typed and sent with packets of seeds to shareholders such as Bulley so that they could feel involved.

Comber wrote from Argentina on 12 October 1925. 'My plan of campaign is to start … with a man and a boy, 6 horses and 2–4 mules and proceed to Las Lajas. Then to cross the watershed …'[19] But, as so often with plant hunters in remote areas, he had problems of transport and food and had 'to fight to keep things going' but he succeeded sufficiently for the Andes Syndicate to back him to go further into Chile on a second expedition. Altogether his finds were small compared to those of the great Asiatic plant hunters, but a good proportion proved garden-worthy. We do not know if any plants at Ness result from his collections. Certainly some Chilean plants growing today in the Royal Botanic Garden Edinburgh are the original plants raised from seeds collected by Comber and Clarence Elliott, who was the next plant hunter Bulley supported in South America.

Clarence Elliott (1881–1969) had collected plants with Farrer, and his travels had ranged as far as the Falkland Islands. He was a nurseryman specialising in alpine and herbaceous plants, having founded the Six Hills Nursery at Stevenage in Hertfordshire. He was an influential alpine gardener, and was to become a founder member of the Alpine Garden Society which now has 13 500 members. When Elliott was planning an expedition to the

Andes for 1929/30, Bulley was one of the 28 subscribers. In today's climate of conservation, the most flabbergasting aspect of this expedition was the scale on which he had to collect, in order that each sponsor should receive a worthwhile amount. For example, he dug up 2500 bulbs of the beautiful lily, *Leucocoryne ixiodes odorata* 'Glory of the Sun', which is only found in Chile. This meant that even though Bulley only had a half-share in the expedition, he received 100 bulbs.[20] They were collected in October 1929 from the Coquimbo region of Chile, and received an award of merit from the RHS, so Bulley must have been delighted with his new loot. Indeed, he was so pleased that he took a half-share in Elliott's next Californian expedition!

Altogether funding expeditions organised by others was a very pleasant pastime in Bulley's retirement. And in the 1930s, Bulley took shares in expeditions of a young gardener working at Clarence Elliott's Six Hills Nursery. This was Edward K Balls (1892–1984). In 1932 Bulley was one of his 24 subscribers for seed from an expedition to the mountains of Persia (Iran), when seed was collected of the first Dionysias ever seen in cultivation.[21] Bulley was judged to be one of those 'most likely to grow Dionysias, if such a thing is possible.'[22] It was a tribute to his experience, for these pretty, primula-like flowers are found only in the Middle East, mainly in Iran and Afghanistan, and they are tantalisingly difficult to grow in cultivation.

(Top) Leucocoryne ixioides, *a lily endemic to Chile. A K Bulley received 100 bulbs from Clarence Elliott's 1929 expedition.*

(Above) Dionysia curviflora, *a pretty, pink-flowered alpine from Iran. It grows only up to 5 cm high, even in flower.*

(Right) Edward K Balls *(1892–1984).*

Bulley continued to sponsor Balls on at least five more expeditions: to Turkey in 1933, '34 and '35, to Morocco in 1936, and to Greece in 1937. By then Bulley was 76 years old, and it was his last recorded sponsorship of a plant hunter before the Second World War descended.

A fine feature of these latter years was Bulley's continued support for young men who wanted to 'have a go' at plant hunting. As the syndicates of gardeners became larger and larger, his personal influence declined, but the spirit was there. At the time of his first subscription to Balls, in 1932, it was nearly 30 years since Bulley had started George Forrest on his plant-hunting career. It was also the year of Forrest's death. The wheel had gone full circle. Forrest had died but Bulley, on the last lap of his own journey through life, was encouraging the next generation of plant hunters.

The contented gardener

In 1922, when the RHS offered Bulley the award of the Victoria Medal of Honour (but he declined), the Swiss expert on alpine plants, Henri Correvon, gave Bulley his own personal tribute. He gave him one of his books, *Champs et Bois Fleuris*, and inside Correvon wrote, 'Bulley, le grand jardinier.'

The head gardener, Mr Josiah Hope (with cap), collected seeds for A K Bulley in the Alps, c. 1930

Happily, this was followed by Bulley enjoying 20 years of gardening in his retirement. He continued to introduce some of Forrest's flowers, and he exhibited *Pieris formosa forrestii* (Plate 4). It stands triumphant in Ness Gardens to this day and was one of the first ever to grow in England. It is a splendid bush (Plate 5).

Bulley also instructed his head gardener, Mr Josiah Hope, to make a pocket-sized booklet, listing his surplus seeds, to be sent to anyone interested.[23] It was kept up to date yearly and listed 350–500 species. The occasional numbered one, such as *Aster* 22775 Forrest and *Gentiana* 59417 Rock, had not yet been wholly identified. So some seeds were fresh gatherings of well-known plants, while others were new from recent expeditions to China (J J Rock) or Europe and the Middle East (W E Siehe). If anyone fancied a particular plant, they ticked the list and waited for their free seed.

W E Siehe (1859–1928)

In turn, Bulley continued to 'cadge another plant' or say 'I am a petitioner, when you have a piece to share', often in exchange for his own cuttings. When Major F C Stern of Highdown in Sussex enquired of his *Paeonia forrestii*, Bulley replied, 'It is quite possibly the only plant in the country,'[24] and he made a memo to send a piece to him in the autumn. He also swapped two plants of *Isopyrum grandiflorum* for two plants of Stern's *Meconopsis grandis*. Bulley's letter to Stern in 1932 sounded like an old refrain which might have been written at any time in the previous 40 years:

> An idea has occurred to me. We are both rather keen on out of the way plants … I will send you a list of some good things … You are sure to have good things … so we should both be gainers.[25]

Always glad to exchange new ideas, Bulley continued, 'Do you ever come north? It would be a pleasure to go round the garden with you and absorb some of your wisdom. I am, at present, trying an exciting experiment with cotton wool as a means of getting *Eritrichium nanum* through the winter. So far it is a shining success.'[26] This blue, forget-me-not-like flower is sometimes called the 'King of the Alps', but it is notoriously difficult to grow. Major Stern was obviously fascinated by Bulley's idea. Three years later, at a conference on rock gardens and rock plants in London, he recalled in discussion, 'Mr Bulley once told me to cover it with cotton wool all winter and so kid it it was covered with snow …'[27]

Persevering with difficult plants was like a series of adventures in his garden. While plant hunters had their adventures on 'the eaves of the world, the frightful lonely mountains', experimenting in his garden brought Bulley contentment and a sense of satisfaction.

Thus Bulley, the quintessential plantsman, enjoyed his old age. New ideas were still kindled by curiosity and a sense of fun. Each experiment brought keen anticipation, spiced with the possibility of success! As ever, he shared his enthusiasms, exchanged ideas, and inspired and stimulated others to follow on.

As he was dying peacefully in his home at Ness Gardens in 1942, his sense of future continuity was shared with his wife in the words of Thomas Gray's Elegy written in a Country Churchyard:

> Ev'n from the tomb the voice of Nature cries,
> Ev'n in our Ashes live their wonted Fires.[28]

There is continuity in a special way at Ness Gardens, and from recent plant hunting expeditions, many plants, first discovered by his plant hunters, are being re-introduced into gardens throughout the world.

Part IV

Overview

~ 11 ~

Bulley's Contribution

*To live in a great idea means to treat the impossible as thought it were
possible ... When an idea and a character meet, things arise which fill the
world with wonder* (GOETHE, QUOTED BY BULLEY).

Patronage

For centuries the worlds of music, art and horticulture have benefited from
patrons who have enabled composers, artists and plant hunters to enrich us
through their work. But patronage has changed. During the nineteenth century
the role of royalty and aristocrats gradually gave way to the new rich of the
Industrial Revolution and the world of commerce. Railway building financed
Tchaikovsky through Madame von Meck. The sewing machine fortune of the
Singer family supported Stravinsky and Poulenc, and the family nursery firm
of Veitch financed plant hunters. And in the twentieth century, the dynamic
Liverpool cotton broker, A K Bulley, became a patron of plant hunters. Bulley
was one of the last powerful patrons of plant hunters before the pattern and
circumstances of twentieth-century sponsorship changed again.[1]

The cornerstone of Bulley's policy was the establishment of a plant nursery
which sponsored its own plant hunters from 1904. This was timely because
patronage for British plant hunters was perilously poised. No government
money was available, and the RHS was absorbed in its centenary celebrations,
fund-raising for its new hall in London and its new garden at Wisley. Without
Veitch sponsoring Wilson and Purdom, and Bees' sole sponsorship of Forrest,
Ward and Cooper, there might have been no British-based plant hunters in
south-east Asia early this century.

Strong links developed between the plant nurseries who obtained the seeds,
and the botanic gardens who named the plants. Bees became to Edinburgh
what Veitch was to Kew. The friendship between Bulley and Balfour was
fundamental to this liaison. It meant that Bulley's extraordinary enthusiasm
and drive were well directed and advised. In turn, after Forrest went to China
in 1904, the horticultural and taxonomic expertise in Edinburgh improved
with each plant collection sent to it by Bulley's plant hunters. In 1919 Bulley
(and in lesser degree Major Lionel de Rothschild) further enhanced
Edinburgh's position by presenting to the botanic garden the herbarium of the
late Hector Léveillé.[2] In Paris Léveillé had described and named many Chinese
plants, some inaccurately, but the names were already in the literature. There

was added confusion when the same species were given different names by French and British botanists. At last this could be sorted out in the Royal Botanic Garden, Edinburgh, which became pre-eminent in the study of Sino-Himalayan plants, a position it still holds today. No wonder that Balfour wrote to Bulley, on his retirement from being the director, 'I carry happy memories and none more vivid and cherished than that of my coming in touch with you and of all your many kindnesses and your generosity in promoting our cause.'[3]

Bulley fought keen competition from the USA. 'The Americans' were very anxious to get Léveillé's herbarium when Bulley and Rothschild stepped in to purchase it for Edinburgh. Earlier this century Professor Charles Sprague Sargent, director of the Arnold Arboretum in Boston, and Dr David Fairchild of the US Government, began to entice British plant hunters to work for them in China. They promised more money and the possibility of permanent positions. Indeed, in 1906, E H Wilson was won over to work for Professor Sargent and ultimately Wilson settled in America as director of the Arnold Arboretum.[4] Otherwise Bulley won the battles. Once Bulley had launched Forrest, Sargent and Fairchild both showed interest in him, but in 1910 Bulley quietly made it possible for Forrest to return to his favourite area of Yunnan, and thereafter his collections kept on coming to Britain. In November 1910 Fairchild also made enquiries of Ward and kept in contact with him, but Bulley wrote successfully 'out of the blue' and launched Ward in plant collecting. Bulley took up the British baton in the race to introduce Chinese plants to Britain and America and he kept professional plant hunters in the field when other sponsors faded away. The firm of Veitch lost confidence in the amount of floral riches in China, and was winding down its operations anyway. So, with temporary US inactivity in China, too, Bulley approached his peak of patronage unrivalled.

The First World War brought the end of Bulley's sole patronage of plant hunters. But he had provided a critical lead and stimulated interest so that other wealthy gardeners took up the challenge. They saw the value of the new plants from the East, and with this new impetus they began to club together to sponsor plant hunters in syndicates. There were some advantages. The cost and responsibility were shared, and also the growth of the seeds, and the exhibition of the new plants. It was a flexible system, in which gardeners could subscribe different amounts, specialise in the growth of different plants, and grow them in different conditions to maximise success. As for the plant hunters, for Forrest there was relief from feeling himself the servant of commerce. For others it was an extra strain if, like Farrer, they had to find their own subscribers. One drawback was the necessity to collect much more seed, though this did not worry an experienced man like Forrest. Ward, with his more academic approach, circumvented the problem by obtaining grants as his mainstay. But Bulley subscribed to expeditions which ranged from his joint patronage with one other wealthy gardener, R Cory, a coal distributor in South Wales, to expeditions with 24 subscribers (for E K Balls) and 28 subscribers (for Clarence Elliott). One can see how this led to the organisation, today, of teams of collectors as well as subscribers, to ease the load for everyone.

Bulley and plant distributions

By 1924 Bulley had sponsored plant hunters in the Sino-Himalaya for 20 years. These were some of the most exciting years known in plant discovery because the plant hunters searched the richest flora in the northern temperate zone. From those discoveries we now know that almost half of all *Primula* species grow in the eastern Sino-Himalaya and most of them can be found nowhere else.[5] The wealth of rhododendrons utterly astonished the plant hunters. The dense concentration of species led to theories that rhododendrons and primulas may have evolved in this part of the World.

Imagine a map of a vast area, in which even the sources of some rivers were unknown, the height and alignment of all the mountains uncertain. How would you decide where to send a plant hunter? As a patron, Bulley was willing to do his homework, ask advice and send successive plant hunters to different areas to try and optimise each hunter's chance of finding something new. Sending George Forrest to Yunnan was a brilliant beginning. For in Yunnan the mountains yielded a large variety of rhododendrons and primulas, and an abundance of other flowers whose variety seemed to exceed that of the terrain, climate and soils. Many primulas, for example, were found to have very local distributions. *Primula forrestii* is centred on one mountain range within the

Plant hunting in the Sino-Himalaya sponsored by A K Bulley / Bees Ltd.

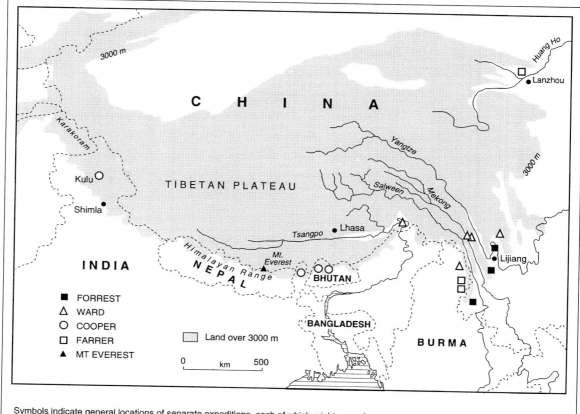

Symbols indicate general locations of separate expeditions, each of which might spread over several mountain ranges

northern loop of the Yangtze river, and does not spread far beyond these bounds. *Primula bulleyana* (Plate 11) and *P. vialii* (Plate 9) are more widespread, but still found mainly within south-west China. Similarly local distributions occur elsewhere. When Ward and Cawdor went to south-east Tibet, they opened up a new area rich in alpine plants about half-way between Sikkim and Yunnan. Some of the primulas they found there, such as *P. cawdoriana*, *P. alpicola* and *P. florindae* (Plate 12), are exclusive to south-east Tibet. And in the heights of the Himalayas there are many species of fairly local distribution, as discoveries in Bhutan and Everest showed. Only by sending plant hunters to different areas of the Sino-Himalaya was it possible to find all these species.

On the other hand, some species were found in more and more areas. The most widely distributed primula, *P. sikkimensis*, is now known to grow extensively in the Himalayas from Nepal in the west through Sikkim, Bhutan and south-east Tibet, to Assam and Burma, and east into Yunnan, China.

As with many primulas, so with blue poppies. If Bulley had relied on only one geographical source for seeds, he would never have grown so many

The isolated distribution of primulas first found with sponsorship of A K Bulley/Bees Ltd.

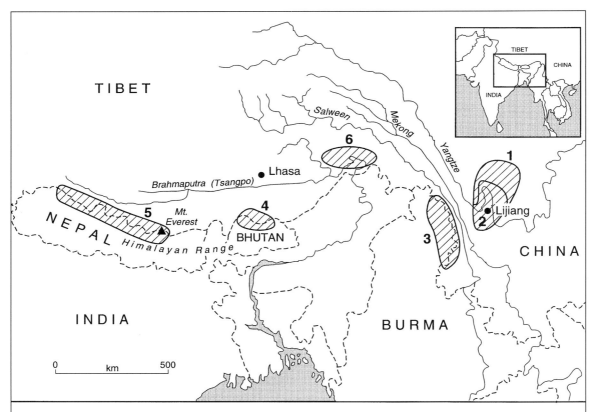

Different species (and plant hunters)

1	Primula bulleyana (G. Forrest, 1906)	**4**	Primula eburnea (R.E. Cooper, 1915)
2	Primula forrestii (G. Forrest, 1906)	**5**	Primula wollastonii (A.F.R. Wollaston, 1921)
3	Primula burmanica (F.K. Ward 1914)	**6**	Primula cawdoriana (F.K. Ward, 1924)

With thanks to John Richards

species in his garden. For in the wild, the rich blue flowers of *Meconopsis grandis* grow only in the eastern Himalaya. The paler blue, harebell poppy, *M. quintuplinervia*, grows in north China and overlaps only slightly with *M. betonicifolia*. Bulley obtained seed of all three only over a long period of time and through different people. He gained seed of the first from native collectors in Sikkim about 1899, the second via Farrer in Kansu in 1914–15, and the last from Ward in Tibet in 1924.

Working out a plant's distribution is like fitting together the pieces of a mighty jigsaw, made more complicated because one plant may have been given two or more names! New discoveries continue today. But a lot of progress was made even in Bulley's lifetime. For example, Bulley was interested in the tree paeonies of China in the 1890s. His plant hunters found several wild forms, and in 1946, Major F C Stern produced the first map of the distribution of wild tree paeonies in western China.[6] Considering that paeonies were first known only from gardens along the Chinese coast, this was a big step forward.

By wise patronage Bulley contributed to our knowledge of plant geography as well as to our gardens. And our gardens were all the more enriched by the plant hunters gathering seed over such a wide area of the Sino-Himalaya.

Acceptance of the new plants

Bulley furthered his contribution by introducing and advertising new hardy herbaceous and alpine species in Bees' catalogues. 'We are noted for Primulas. Our new introductions from China are world-famous. For the first time, we are offering seeds of these faultlessly beautiful plants in 1d packets.' Bees' seed catalogue of 1912 was making every effort to reach a wide market, and by then some of its award-winning primulas, *P. bulleyana*, *P. forrestii*, *P. littoniana* (syn. *P. vialii*) and *P. malacoides* were already in an encyclopaedia of gardening.[7] They were being avidly absorbed into ornamental gardening, and in the middle of the First World War, Bees Ltd was selling new crosses of primulas (Plate 10) and collections of hardy primulas, including primulas collected by Wilson and Forrest.

However, each of the popular genera of primulas, gentians and poppies included species that were difficult to retain in cultivation, or were only grown by skilled enthusiasts. But among all the disappointments and failures there have emerged flowers of such beauty and ease of cultivation that between them they have been absorbed into every part of the garden, from the greenhouse to the alpine house, from the rock garden to bog and water gardens. They have extended the colour range and length of flowering seasons, and provided ideal material for developing fashions in garden design such as 'drifts' of flowers (as shown in Plate 13), and woodland gardening.

Wide publicity in horticultural and gardening journals greatly assisted the acceptance of new plants. Gardeners were encouraged to experiment. For example, the beauty of many new flowers was demonstrated in a spate of pictures in *Curtis's Botanical Magazine* in the 1920s. These included *Primula bulleyana* (1924) (Plate 11), *Buddleja farreri* (1924), *P. beesiana* (1925), *Viburnum grandiflorum* (1925) (Plate 29), *Roscoea cautleoides* (1926), *Geranium farreri* (1926) and *Jasminum beesianum* (1926) (Plate 15).

Plant hunters themselves also longed to persuade gardeners to grow the new plants. Farrer's book, *The English Rock Garden* (1919), gave impetus to alpine gardening. Others had become enthralled by the range of rhododendrons, especially when rhododendron enthusiasts such as Williams and Rothschild followed Bulley in sponsorship. E H M Cox, after collecting with Farrer, wrote *Rhododendrons for Amateurs* (1924). Ward wrote *Rhododendrons for Everyone* (1926) 'in the hope of interesting a larger public in rhododendrons'. They succeeded, as the Asian species largely supplanted the American ones, and hybridisation brought many stunning cultivars.

Contemporary gardening books could hardly keep pace with the influx of new plants introduced by plant hunters sponsored by Bulley and others. Many new editions of books were needed. In her book, *The Herbaceous Garden*, Lady Martineau explained in her fourth edition (1934) that 'so many new plants have been discovered, and new varieties of old plants introduced, that in justice to my readers, I have found a complete revision necessary.' There was a new chapter, 'Lilies and New Plants', including lilies, nomocharis, gentians and meconopses, many of them from the Sino-Himalaya. She commented, 'It is difficult to imagine our summer gardens without those Meconopses.' In picking Forrest's *Gentiana sino-ornata* and Ward's *Meconopsis betonicifolia*, she wrote, 'Their popularity is indeed deserved.'

T W Sanders' *Encyclopaedia of Gardening* also reflected the changing garden scene. From 1895, when Bulley was on the verge of buying land at Ness, to 1931, there were 22 editions. A comparison of two of Gertrude Jekyll's books shows the new opportunities for landscaping, too. In *Wall and Water Gardens* (1901), she mentioned a few Asian primulas in three paragraphs. By 1933, in an eighth revised edition, she invited G C Taylor to write a whole new chapter on 'The Asiatic Primulas'. This emphasised the prospect of entirely new garden pictures by using hardy primulas in different settings, from the waterside garden to the dappled shade of woodlands (see Plate 13). Also, combining primulas with other new introductions such as rhododendrons provided 'pictures of the most enchanting loveliness ... Broad drifts of Candelabra primulas, such as *Primula bulleyana* framed by bold masses of Rhododendrons and Azaleas ... a setting of matchless beauty.'[8]

Bulley was a foremost patron and catalyst in this golden age of the early twentieth century. He loved to experiment and to start a new project. He founded a famous nursery, Bees Ltd, gave a fresh momentum to plant hunting in the Sino-Himalaya, and was highly influential in the introduction of new alpine and hardy plants. Mrs Bulley threatened to write her husband's epitaph as: 'Bulley, his fortunes and misfortunes.' There is no doubt that his fortunes left their legacy in British gardens.

Epilogue

A hundred years on

My dear Mildred,
A wee little bit of a damsel ... came to us this morning.[1]

Agnes Lois Bulley was born. Arthur Bulley, the proud father, was passing on the good news to his sister in December 1901. Lois adored her parents, and it was Lois who was to ensure the future of Ness Gardens.

When Bulley died in 1942, after 44 years at Ness, the future of his garden was threatened. Weeds invaded during the Second World War and Lois feared that developers would follow. She resolved to find a way to keep it 'as a practical and fitting tribute to his memory'. Eventually she was inspired to present the whole estate of 60 acres (24 ha), including the family home, Mickwell Brow, to the University of Liverpool. This gift came with an endowment of £75 000 in 1948, and it was the largest bequest the university had received other than its Cohen library. Furthermore, one important condition was that part of the gardens should always be open to the public.

Lois Bulley, 3 October 1902.

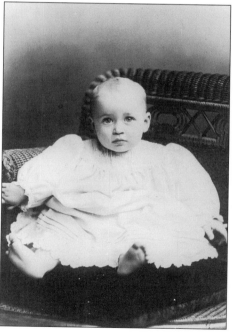

It is a happy quirk of ancestry that Lois is distantly related, on her mother's side, to the man who planned the Imperial Botanic Garden at St Petersburg![2] That garden was thriving when Bulley founded Ness Gardens a hundred years ago, and he held its seed lists in great esteem early this century. Thanks to his daughter's benevolence after his death, his own gardens were to become a university botanic garden. Her father's work continues in a special, totally befitting way.

Within the gardens there is a strong awareness of Bulley's vision. The vibrant core of the work is experimental, as it always has been. The advancement of knowledge continues side by side with people's appreciation of the beauty and peace of the garden. The displays of flowers provide pleasure and education, as the plants are labelled with their name and, where known, their place of origin. Seed exchange continues across the world, helping in the spread and conservation of rare plants.

Senior staff are continuing Bulley's work of plant introduction, helping to discover varieties suited to cultivation in Britain. The deputy director, Dr Hugh McAllister, has collected seed in the Lake Baikal area of the Russian Federation.

The curator, Peter Cunnington, joined in the 1994 Alpine Garden Society China Expedition partly following in the footsteps of George Forrest and Kingdon Ward. They had a small taste of the privations and joys of those great plant hunters. They collected alpine seeds, a proportion of them now growing at Ness, and they revelled in the beauty of the flowers in the wild. Acres of a wonderful blue haze turned out to be multitudes of *Gentiana sino-ornata*, surely one of the most beautiful and popular of George Forrest's discoveries. Forrest's collections of this species first flowered at Ness in 1912. Its flower is the logo for Ness Botanic Gardens, symbolising the important role of these gardens in the introduction of many beautiful plants to this country.

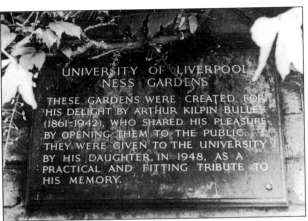

Memorial plaque.

Gradually the work and size of the gardens has been expanded. More and more fields have been brought into use, until the gardens now occupy 62 acres (25 ha) and more than half this area is open to the public. The grounds have been beautifully planted and landscaped by Kenneth Hulme OBE, the director for 32 years (1957–89). His artistic flair has brought fluency of lines and sweeping vistas, and the use of a wide range of species and cultivars has lengthened the flowering season and improved the colour range all year. The separate gardens of Bulley have been integrated into a greater whole.

The present director, Professor Robert H Marrs, holds the university's new Bulley Chair of Applied Plant Biology and there are new laboratories in Bulley's former home. Marr's work even includes experimental trials on bracken on Thurstaston Common, in an attempt to restore heathland on land which Bulley helped to purchase for the National Trust in 1926.

Many of the poplars which Bulley planted as shelter belts have died. Others stand above the Dee marshes, reminiscent of a Monet painting, eloquent of the past, and still shimmering in the sunlight. The pond which Bulley dug in the rock garden is one of the most popular parts of the gardens. It was dug at the time that Monet painted the water lilies at Giverny. And just as people enjoy those paintings, so Ness Botanic Gardens welcomes infinitely more visitors than Bulley could have dreamed of. He would be delighted to see the appreciation of the beautiful plants which his plant hunters brought back as seed. And *Primula bulleyana* (Plate 7) self-seeds around the pond as if it has always been there.

Bulley's radio talk

Sometimes you may stroll round the rock garden and try and recapture the past. Imagine being there in the 1930s when Bulley was pottering in his garden, a bit stiff from a fall in the Alps, but as spry as ever, and talking in his lively and frank way. This script is of a 20-minute North Regional broadcast which Bulley gave on the wireless one February evening in 1934.[3] *The Radio Times* states: '7.0 Mr. A.K. Bulley: The Fascination of Alpines.' He was 73 years old and keen to take advantage of this relatively new means of communication to share one of his enthusiasms.

THE FASCINATION OF ALPINES

The announcer: Probably no man living in the North of England has collected and grown so many strange plants from foreign parts as Mr. A.K. Bulley. Tonight, he will speak on his rock garden in Cheshire, and give listeners some useful hints on growing Alpines.

Mr Bulley: My job tonight is to suggest to you that you might be well advised to try growing Alpine plants in your garden. For this advice there are two excellent and obvious reasons. Firstly, Alpine plants are in general small plants, and so you can get more of them into a small space; secondly, owing to their smallness, they can stand wind much better than herbaceous plants, and you are lucky if your garden is not sometimes wind-swept. But the smallness of the plants doesn't prevent their making a large subject. And it is easy to understand this, when you realise that with the exception of a few mountains near the Poles, which are always covered with ice or snow, and of a few mountains in deserts, where rain seldom falls, Alpine plants come from practically all the great mountain ranges of the world. And indeed they do not come only from mountains. For there is a certain correspondence between altitude and latitude; and so, as they move further north, Alpine plants are content with lower and lower elevations, until finally you meet, without surprise, plants to which you have been accustomed on the mountains in Switzerland, growing quite happily at sea level in Spitzbergen.

Now when you consider what this means, how many soils it covers, how many kinds of rock, the varied aspects, and the conditions of moraines and bogs and running streams, you will realise that a rock garden, adequate for all these possibilities, has got to be a huge affair. As a matter of fact, I believe that the rockery in the Edinburgh Botanic Garden covers an acre and a quarter, and for anything I know there may be still bigger. A trifling reflection which may occur to you is, that to make and keep in good order a rockery of this kind, you will have to be a millionaire.

Well, I am not going to trouble you tonight with reflections suitable for a millionaire rockery. I am going to imagine that you have only a small garden, and that you can afford only a small expenditure upon it.

And now, what sort of a rockery are you to put up, on which to grow Alpine plants? Well, let me break it to you, as quietly as maybe, that if you will take my advice, you won't put up any rockery at all. For what is a rockery in a small garden? Always, or almost always (for there is such a thing as a sunken rockery), it is a raised mound of soil with a good many big stones put into it. Sometimes these stones are put in idiotically, serving no purpose, unless ugliness is a purpose; sometimes wisely and well, so as to throw the rain into the interior of the rockery, instead of letting it run away down the surface; but whether wisely or foolishly, covering a certain amount of your available space with stones, which might be better covered by plants. And indeed a rockery of this kind is not only a waste of space; it is also a very real danger to your plants. For if you can't make it big enough to hold the moisture, then when a drought comes, such as we had last summer, the rockery will dry out, and you and your plants will part company in the most heart-breaking way.

Of course there are alternatives. You may prefer to use your garden for herbaceous plants, and very beautiful they are. But they have two drawbacks. They are big, and so take up too much of your space, and some of the best need staking. Or you may grow shrubs, and a shrub garden has this advantage, that it is the cheapest of all gardens. Once you get your shrub established, it will go on growing more or less forever, becoming year by year more beautiful, and to a large extent doing its own weeding. The real trouble about shrubs is just this fact that they grow. If only they would get to a reasonable size, and then stop, I should recommend them to you, because they are so cheap and easy. But shrubs will seldom behave in a reasonable way. I have been gardening for many years, yet even now, I cannot get myself to plant shrubs sufficiently far apart, they look so utterly miserable and desolate. But sure enough they grow, and grow, and grow, and presently they are into one another, perhaps in some delightful unplanned picture, but more generally, in deep discordance and murderous strife. Therefore I recommend you to grow Alpines on, at any rate, part of your space. But you may well say how is it possible here in England and not in Spitzbergen, to grow in a garden, practically at sea level, plants which come from high mountains; and the answer is that if you try it, you will, with most Alpine plants, find no particular difficulty.

I suppose that the main reason why Alpine plants grow on the Alps, is just the reason which makes them so useful for your garden. They are small, low-growing, air-loving things, and in the long grass of the lowlands they would soon be killed; but on the short turf of the mountains, kept still shorter by sheep, they can live and flourish; and as in your garden they will not be overwhelmed by long grass, you will find that they will live and flourish there also.

Now I have told you that I don't recommend you to make a rockery. How then are you to grow these delightful, free flowering and very showy Alpine plants? Well the method is extraordinarily simple. Make three flat beds, in any shape you like. Personally I think that 8 ft. is a good width, from path to path. If you put flat stepping stones down the middle of the bed, you will be able to get quite close to all your plants, and will need the minimum of space for paths. Let the surface of these beds be about 4 inches above the level of the paths. This is to ensure the drainage, which is essential for Alpines. Into the first bed put a good deal of lime; you can do it in the form of limestone chippings, or of old mortar from houses that are being pulled down. Make the second bed of any soil you have which is not limey. Into your third bed put plenty of peat, for plants (most North American plants for instance) which look on lime as poison, and are entirely happy only in peat. These three beds are exceedingly easy to keep clean , and on them you will be able to grow nine-tenths of the Alpine plants with complete success. Have you easy access to fallen leaves in autumn, particularly oak and beech leaves? If you have, dig in lots of them when you make the beds; stack the balance, and dig in more whenever you get a chance. They are of the greatest value for retaining moisture in the soil, and may make all the odds when drought comes.

Increase your stock as rapidly as possible, and so enable yourself to enjoy perhaps the choicest delight that can be got out of gardening, the giving of your good things to your friends – and to your enemies.

It is desirable that there should be for your beds a certain amount of shade, both permanent and temporary. You can get the permanent shade from dwarf shrubs, or from such a plant as the Algerian Iris (*Iris stylosa*), an evergreen that will not only provide you with shade, but will give you a succession of large, beautiful and sweet-scented flowers, from late autumn, through all west wind days in winter, to well on in the spring. By temporary shade I mean that there are certain plants, primulas for instance, which cannot stand anything in the way of drought, and you must be able, whenever drought comes, to help them with some temporary shading. Gorse, broom, heather, bracken, any of these will do the job. Cut branches or fronds and lay them loosely over the plants. The idea is to give partial shade, but to let air in.

Another tip. Err on the side of planting closely, rather than far apart. Don't leave spaces uncovered, for uncovered space means weeds, and the less weeding the better. And now that we have got everything ready, what are you going to plant?

Well if you live in London your choice is made easy. You can go to Kew, or to the fortnightly shows of the Royal Horticultural Society, and pick things you like. The same is true if you are near to Edinburgh, or Dublin, or a few other places where there are fine Botanic Gardens. Or perhaps you have a friend who already grows these plants, or perhaps there is some nursery near where you can see them. It is highly desirable to see plants for yourself and to please your own taste. If there is no assistance of this kind in your neighbourhood, you must trust to books (there are some excellent ones), or to catalogues. Well the writers of catalogues are but human. You mustn't therefore be greatly surprised if whites tend to be described as pure whites or snow whites; pinks as shell pinks; and if now and again some vile and vicious magenta comes out of the printing room as royal purple.

Apropos of colours, I'll tell you rather a queer thing. I am an extraordinarily innocent and unsuspecting person. I am doubtless believing wads of nonsense, on the usual and admirable ground that believing saves thinking. I order plants every year on catalogue descriptions. But one time, for some unknown reason, I developed suspicion about the colour phrase shell pink. I thought it needed checking off. So I went to the shell room in the South Kensington Museum, and worked thoroughly through it. Of course I had a riotously good time, for it's a magnificent collection. But as I slowly passed from case to case, the impression deepened on me, that the majority — the overwhelming majority — of the pink shells, had their pink largely suffused with blue. And I don't like blue pink. It reminds me of cold fingers and underfed children. At the end, I was doubtful whether I had seen a single shell which could compare, and not fear the comparison, with the flawless pink of the dog rose, as you have so often seen it in country lanes. You don't believe that? Good. Well, try and experiment for yourself, and see what conclusion you come to.

Now two pieces of advice. Firstly, plant for succession. You will find that the majority of Alpine plants flower in April, May and June. This means that the few which flower earlier and later than these months have exceptional value for your garden.

Secondly, get your plants into clumps or even masses. A smaller number of first class kinds is much more effective than a larger number of second class kinds. The late Reginald Farrer, who worked so devotedly for Alpine plants and their lovers, was dreadfully down on massing, which he thought smacked of the factory. He called it 'Alpine carpet-bedding'. Perhaps the term is just. But when I look round, I note that Mother Nature does it herself, on a huge scale. She does it with heather and bluebells and poppies and buttercups and broom, and hosts of other fine things. So that if I sin, I sin in good company, in fact with one of the best people, and that is always so dreadfully agreeable.

But you needn't bother with who thinks this, or who thinks that. I invite you all to visit my garden, where you will see the actual thing and can judge for yourselves. Come once a month, come once a fortnight, come whenever the fancy takes you. From May and earlier, to September and later, the picture is always changing. The garden is open all day and all night, and there is no charge. Just walk straight in and, I hope, enjoy yourselves. The garden is about a mile and a half from Neston railway station. It is nine miles below Chester, on the estuary of the Dee.

And now you are ready to make your choice. What a choice it is. You may perhaps begin with the aubretias, though there are some Alpines which flower still earlier, and I must admit that there are colours in the aubretia family which simply give me the creeps. But then I am a colour faddist; so pay no attention to that. There are the gentians with their cold but ravishing blues; the saxifrages, typical rock plants, which will grow all right without rocks; delicately tinted, shade-loving primulas; the edelweiss, whose natural home is on precipices, but which will flourish in your limestone bed; the sun roses, in sheets of burning colour; the dwarf phloxes, which will destroy all weeds; the harebells, flowering late; pale and dark blue speedwells; violas which will often flower through the whole season, and a host of lovely things besides.

You probably don't guess how long the show can be continued. But there is an exquisite little cyclamen from Naples, a gentian from China, and a saxifrage from Japan, which flower in late September and October.

You will notice that so far I have exercised superb restraint and have not urgently recommended to you any particular plant. But by way of a change I am now going to recommend one, which is also a later flowerer. It is a crocus. Do you know and grow *Crocus speciosus?* If you don't, make a note to buy a few bulbs (they are quite cheap) next July. Plant them, and in September they will show you just what a crocus can do when it really lays itself out on the job. Dwarf, dainty and cool, it contrasts in a striking way with the big, overbearing, hot herbaceous plants, which form such a large part of the September display. It is, to my thinking, far more beautiful than any of the spring crocuses.

I see that my time is still not quite up, and I shall devote what remains to you, the lucky ones, who already have beautiful gardens, and perhaps rockeries. I want you to throw them open. It is your delightful privilege. Begin as tentatively as you like, with a few hours on one day a week, and extend to all hours, every day of the week. Let the entry be free. It is all very well making a charge and giving the proceeds to a charity. That is it is all very well for the charity. But the people who have simply no beauty at all in their lives, and who have the greatest need of your garden, can't afford a charge of any kind. Don't shut them out. I don't want you to be under any illusions. You will certainly get disappointments. Inconsiderate people will throw fags and sticky sweet paper about; children will want to climb on your rockery; dogs to stray over your flower beds. And you may occasionally be visited by a thief. Well, recognise that these things will happen and prepare for them.

You can have receptacles for the fags and the paper. You can say that children will only be admitted with some older person to look after them. You may bar dogs, except on leash. And as for the occasional thief, don't put your rare plants and your single specimens in the public part of the garden. If you have things in clumps, the loss of an occasional plant won't ruin you. It is miserable that everything nowadays should be, customarily, valued in terms of money. You will get no money dividends by throwing your garden open, but you will get tremendous dividends in happiness. Sharing is worth a hundred of monopolising. It will make you feel jolly to see people going round your garden; and if you mix with them unbeknownst, you will hear some very nice things. And every now and again, you will get the exceptional pleasure of seeing someone like yourself, who goes round really understanding and appreciating the difficulties you have met, and the successes you have scored.

It's fine.   Start this spring.   Goodnight.

ᑌᐧNotes ᑎᐧ
and References

Abbreviations

Sources of unpublished material and journals

Edin.	Archives of the Royal Botanic Garden Edinburgh. (File *HERB/1/34/1*, Bulley–Balfour letters, unless stated otherwise.)
Dub.	Archives of the National Botanic Gardens, Dublin
Kew	Archives of the Royal Botanic Gardens, Kew
RGS	Archives of the Royal Geographical Society
RHS	Archives of the Royal Horticultural Society
EE	*Everest Expedition Collections (RGS)*
G.C.	*Gardeners' Chronicle*
Bull AGS	*Bulletin of the Alpine Garden Society*
Dir. Corr.	*Directors' Correspondence (Kew)*

Preface

1. Reid, M, *The Plant Hunters*, London, 1858, p.1.
2. Hulme, J K, *Ness Gardens*, University of Liverpool Botanic Garden, 1987, p.9.

Introduction. Liverpool: The Gateway to the Empire

1. Lord Stanley, MP replying to a toast at a banquet, *Documents connected with the opening of the Free Public Library, Liverpool*, Liverpool Record Office, 1861, p.51.
2. Thompson, G, 'The Ambassador of Commerce' in the Foreword to the Supplement to the *Liverpool Daily Post*, 7 July 1924.
3. Parkinson, C N, *The Rise of the Port of Liverpool*, Liverpool University Press, 1952, p.32.
4. Ibid. p.84.
5. Baines, T, *Liverpool in 1859*, Longman & Co, 1859, p.13.
6. *The Book of Liverpool*, Civic Week, 22–29 September 1928, Liverpool.
7. Warhurst, E, 'Liverpool Botanic Gardens' *Lancashire and Cheshire Naturalist*, 1919, p.172.
8. A K Bulley to I B Balfour, 19 October 1896 (Edin.).
9. Hosie, A, *Three Years in Western China*, Philip & Son, 1890.

10. Bourne, F S A, *Report of the Mission to China of the Blackburn Chamber of Commerce 1896–7*, Blackburn, 1898, p.146.
11. *Kew Bulletin 1899*, HMSO, 1901, p.48.

Chapter 1. Bulley's Background: Free-thinking Victorians

1. 'In Memoriam' Funeral records of Liverpool Celebrities, A Bowker & Son, 1876, p.1919.
2. Boulger, D C, *Life of Sir Stamford Raffles*, Charles Knight & Co Ltd, 1973, p.23.
3. Collis, M, *Raffles*, Faber & Faber, 1966, p.149.
4. Meijer, W, 'Saving the World's Largest Flower' *National Geographic* 168, 1985, pp.136–140.
5. Mitchell, P C, *Centenary History of the Zoological Society of London*, 1929, p.2.
6. Conversation with Miss A Lois Bulley. Tape recordings to be lodged in the archives of the University of Liverpool.
7. Counihan, J, 'Mrs Ella Armitage, John Horace Round, G T Clark and Early Norman Castles' *Anglo-Norman Studies*, 8, Battle Conference, Boydell & Brewer, 1985, p.76.
8. Conversation with Miss A L Bulley.
9. *G.C.* 34, 1903, p.42.
10. *G.C.* 37, 1905, p.245.
11. *G.C.* 51, 1912, pp.81–2.
12. Conservation with Miss A L Bulley.
13. Binfield, C, *So Down to Prayers* (1977), J M Dent & Sons Ltd has several references to the Bulley family and their Congregational links.
14. Conversation with Miss A L Bulley.
15. A K Bulley to A Henry, 29 August 1897, *Henry mss* (Dub.).
16. Taylor, S, in *Bulls & Bears* No 20, C Tinling & Co Ltd, 1908.
17. Story told by Miss A L Bulley.
18. R Farrer to E H M Cox, 25 June 1920, *Farrer corresp.* (Edin.).
19. A K Bulley to I B Balfour, 31 May 1896 (Edin.).
20. Steedman, C, *Childhood, Culture and Class in Britain: Margaret McMillan 1860–1931*, London, Virago, 1990, p.84.
21. Minutes of Council, Royal Horticultural Society 29, pp.265, 292.
22. Agnes Whishaw to Alfred Bulley, 1942, personal papers of Miss A L Bulley.

Chapter 2. West Kirby: Springboard to Success

1. A K Bulley to A Henry, 19 November 1926, *Henry mss* (Dub.)
2. Ellison, N F 'A pioneer among field clubs' *Cheshire Life* Feb 1961, p.35.
3. *Proceedings of the Liverpool Naturalists' Field Club*, 1891, p.35.
4. Ibid. 1892, p.37.
5. Ibid. p.49.
6. Green, C T (ed.), *The Flora of the Liverpool District*, Liverpool, 1902.
7. A K Bulley to A Henry, undated fragment c.1897, *Henry mss* (Dub.)
8. Ibid.

9. A K Bulley to Thiselton-Dyer, 7 April 1898, *Dir. Corr. (Eng. Letters)* 81, 1866–1900 (Kew).
10. Ibid. 5 September 1897.
11. Ibid. 7 April 1898.
12. A K Bulley to I B Balfour, 10 April 1898 (Edin.).
13. Ibid. 16 February 1899 (Edin.).
14. A K Bulley to A Henry, undated fragment c.1897, *Henry mss* (Dub.).
15. A K Bulley to I B Balfour, 14 March 1896 (Edin.).
16. Ibid. December 1909.
17. A K Bulley to A Henry, 29 August 1897, *Henry mss* (Dub.).
18. In file with Bulley–Balfour letters (Edin.).
19. Pollock, J C, *The Cambridge Seven*, O.M.F. 1985. Also used was a ms of 'Reminiscences of Eton and Cambridge 1875–1882' by Arthur Polhill, courtesy of Roger Polhill at Kew.
20. Inwards Book, July 1990 (Kew).
21. Pim, S, *The Wood and the Trees* (2nd edn), Boethius Press, 1984, p.225.
22. A Henry to E Gleeson, 29 June 1897, *Gleeson mss*, National Library of Ireland, Dublin.
23. Pim, S, *The Wood and the Trees* (2nd edn), Boethius Press, 1984, p.69.
24. I B Balfour to A K Bulley, 19 October 1896 (Edin.).
25. A K Bulley to I B Balfour, 9 March 1896 (Edin.).
26. Ibid. 11 May 1896.
27. I B Balfour to A K Bulley, 8 September 1897 (Edin.).
28. A K Bulley to I B Balfour, 25 April 1897 (Edin.).
29. I B Balfour to A K Bulley, 28 April 1897 (Edin.).
30. A K Bulley to I B Balfour, 3 March 1900 (Edin.).
31. I B Balfour to A K Bulley, 6 March 1900 (Edin.).
32. A K Bulley to I B Balfour, 31 March 1896 (Edin.).
33. I B Balfour to A K Bulley, 9 June 1896 (Edin.).
34. A K Bulley to I B Balfour, 25 April 1897 (Edin.).
35. Ibid. 18 March 1897.
36. I B Balfour to A K Bulley, 31 March 1897 (Edin.).
37. A K Bulley to I B Balfour, 28 January 1912 (Edin.).
38. Ibid. 13 January 1920.
39. Ibid. 5 April 1897.

Chapter 3. Ness Gardens

1. A K Bulley to I B Balfour, 14 December 1896 (Edin.).
2. All legal documents on the acquisition of land of Ness Botanic Gardens are in the Department of Special Collections and Archives of the University of Liverpool.
3. A Henry to Miss Gleeson, 23 September 1901, *Gleeson mss*, National Library of Ireland, Dublin.
4. I B Balfour to A K Bulley, 23 December 1896 (Edin.).

5. Bulley, A K, 'The Fascination of Alpines', talk broadcast by the BBC, North Regional, 7.00 p.m. 13 February 1934.

6. 'Garden that is never closed' *Garden Work for Amateurs* 1930.

7. In conversation with Hannah Smith (née Jones).

8. Kipling, R, 'The Glory of the Garden' in *Songs for Youth*, Hodder and Stoughton, p.193.

9. Wages Book 1907, Ness Botanic Gardens.

10. A K Bulley to I B Balfour, 27 December 1903 (Edin.).

11. Ibid. 13 January 1913.

12. I B Balfour to A K Bulley, 4 February 1913 (Edin.).

13. A K Bulley to I B Balfour, 21 April 1913 (Edin.).

14. Ibid. 4 June 1913.

15. Ibid. 27 March 1915.

16. Ingwerson, W 'These I have loved' *GC* 9 August 1974, p.2.

17. A K Bulley to I B Balfour, 22 September 1917 (Edin.).

18. I B Balfour to A K Bulley, 24 September 1917 (Edin.).

19. Harley, A, 'Some Chinese and Himalayan Gentians' *Q. Bull AGS* 2, 1933, p.40.

20. Hulme, J K, *Ness Gardens – Bulley's Beginnings to the Present Day*, Ness Gardens, 1987, p.22.

21. Diaries of Charles Pearson, courtesy of Mrs Pat McClelland.

22. 'Garden that is never closed' *Garden Work for Amateurs* 1930.

Chapter 4. George Forrest and Bees Ltd

1. A K Bulley to A Henry, undated fragment, c.1897, *Henry mss* (Dub.).

2. A K Bulley to I B Balfour, 3 March 1900 (Edin.).

3. *GC* 36, 1904, p.198.

4. *Flora & Sylva* 3, 1905, pp.80–1.

5. *GC* 36, 1904, p.240.

6. *Flora & Sylva* 3, 1905, p.191.

7. *Annals of Botany* 20, 1906, p.352.

8. Fairchild, D, *The World was my Garden*, Charles Scribner's Sons, New York and London, 1943, p.157.

9. I B Balfour to A K Bulley, 28 April 1904, *Balfour, I Bayley corresp. Boxfile B* (Edin.).

10. Ibid. 30 April 1904.

11. Blake, W, 'Auguries of Innocence' in *William Blake Poetical Works*, Oxford University Press, 1956, p.171.

12. A K Bulley to I B Balfour, 30 October 1904 (Edin.).

13. A K Bulley to Thiselton-Dyer, 30 October 1904, *Dir. Corr. (Eng. Letters)*, 107, 1901–1905 (Kew).

14. G Forrest to I B Balfour, 3 July 1905, HERB/7/2/2 (Edin.).

15. Ibid. 5 January 1905.

16. A K Bulley to I B Balfour, 9 November 1904 (Edin.).

17. G Forrest to I B Balfour, 3 July 1905, HERB/7/2/2 (Edin.).

18. Ibid. 13 July 1905.

19. I B Balfour to A K Bulley, 17 August 1905, *HERB/7/2/2* (Edin.).
20. A K Bulley to I B Balfour, 19 August 1905, *HERB/7/2/2* (Edin.).
21. I B Balfour to A K Bulley, 21 August 1905, *HERB/7/2/2* (Edin.).
22. A K Bulley to I B Balfour, 2 October 1905, *HERB/7/2/2* (Edin.).
23. Ibid. 24 September 1905.
24. A K Bulley to I B Balfour, 21 November 1906 (Edin.).
25. A K Bulley to D Prain, 24 November 1906, *Dir. Corr. (Eng Letters)* 113, 1906–10 (Kew).
26. *Bees' Cat.* Bees Ltd, Liverpool, 1909, p.14 (Edin.).
27. A K Bulley to I B Balfour, 4 May 1909 (Edin.).
28. Fairchild, D, *The World was my Garden*, Charles Scribner's Sons, New York and London, 1943, p.359.
29. A K Bulley to I B Balfour, 4 May 1909 (Edin.).
30. Ibid. 5 August 1909.
31. Ibid. 5 March 1913.
32. A K Bulley to I B Balfour, 26 January 1909, *HERB/7/2/4* (Edin.).
33. Statement of accounts in *HERB/7/2/4* (Edin.).
34. G.C. 47, 1910, p.418.
35. G Forrest to I B Balfour, 12 July 1910, *HERB/7/2/5* (Edin.).
36. Ibid. 25 April 1910 (Edin.).
37. G Forrest to W W Smith, 24 June 1913, *HERB/1/34/1A* (Edin.).
38. A K Bulley to I B Balfour, 7 December 1910, *HERB/7/2/5* (Edin.).
39. Schlechter, R, in *Notes R B G Edin*, 1909–12, p.108.

Chapter 5. Kingdon Ward: The Search Widens

1. Ward, F K, *The Romance of Plant Hunting* (2nd edn), Arnold, 1933, p.269.
2. I B Balfour to A K Bulley, 14 December 1910 (Edin.).
3. Telegram A K Bulley to I B Balfour, December 1910 (Edin.).
4. Mrs M Ward to Oldfield Thomas, 3 October 1910, *Letters on Mammalia* 16/217 (Natural History Museum).
5. Ward, F K, *The Land of the Blue Poppy*, Cambridge University Press, 1913, p.1.
6. Ward, F K, *Pilgrimage for Plants*, Harrap, 1960, p.26.
7. Ibid. p.27.
8. Ibid. p.12.
9. *Bees' Cat.* No 35, Bees Ltd, Liverpool, 1912, p.16 (Edin.).
10. A K Bulley to I B Balfour, 2 June 1911 (Edin.).
11. Ibid. 28 January 1912 (Edin.).
12. I B Balfour to A K Bulley, 29 January 1912 (Edin.).
13. Ward, F K, *The Land of the Blue Poppy*, Cambridge University Press, 1913.
14. Ward, F K, *Pilgrimage for Plants*, Harrap, 1960, pp.160–1.
15. A K Bulley to I B Balfour, 4 March 1912 (Edin.).
16. Ibid. 14 April 1912.
17. *Bees' Cat.* No 41, Bees Ltd, Liverpool, 1913, p.5 (Edin.).
18. A K Bulley to I B Balfour, 9 August 1912 (Edin.).

19. Ward, F K, *The Land of the Blue Poppy*, Cambridge University Press, 1913 pp.274 −8.

20. A K Bulley to I B Balfour, 2 July 1912 (Edin.).

21. See Taylor, G, *An Account of the Genus Meconopsis*, 1934, Waterstone, 1985, p.99.

22. A K Bulley to I B Balfour, 17 September 1912 (Edin.).

23. Ibid. 24 September 1912.

24. F K Ward to Scott Keltie, 23 November 1912, RGS Corr. Block 1911−20 (RGS).

25. A K Bulley to I B Balfour, 30 December 1912 (Edin.).

26. *Bees' Cat.* No 41, Bees Ltd, Liverpool, 1913 (Edin.).

27. G Forrest to W W Smith, 24 June 1913, HERB/1/34/1A (Edin.).

28. A K Bulley to I B Balfour, 18 June 1913 (Edin.).

29. Ibid. 1 September 1913.

30. Ibid. 27 April 1914.

31. Balfour, I B, *Notes RBG Edinburgh XLI*, 1915, pp.63−4.

Chapter 6. R E Cooper in Sikkim and Bhutan

1. I B Balfour to A K Bulley, 13 September 1912 (Edin.).

2. Ibid.

3. A K Bulley to I B Balfour, 17 September 1912 (Edin.).

4. I B Balfour to A K Bulley, 21 September 1912 (Edin.).

5. A K Bulley to I B Balfour, 3 February 1913 (Edin.).

6. Ibid. 18 June 1913.

7. A K Bulley to I B Balfour, 10 September 1913 (Edin.).

8. Richards, John, *Primula*, B T Batsford Ltd, 1993, p.271.

9. A K Bulley to I B Balfour, 12 April 1915 (Edin.).

10. A K Bulley to A W Hill, 31 May 1914, *China−Plant Collns−cultural prods.* 1853−1914 (Kew).

11. A K Bulley to D Prain, 14 October 1913, *China−Plant Collns−cultural prods.* 1853−1914 (Kew).

12. Ibid. 11 October 1913.

13. Ibid. 14 October 1913.

14. A K Bulley to I B Balfour, 20 October 1913 (Edin.).

15. A K Bulley to D Prain, 14 October 1913, *China−Plant Collns−cultural prods.* 1853−1914 (Kew).

16. A K Bulley to I B Balfour, 22 November 1913 (Edin.).

17. A K Bulley to D Prain, 22 February 1914, *China−Plant Collns−cultural prods.* 1853−1914 (Kew).

18. A K Bulley to I B Balfour, 30 May 1914 (Edin.).

19. A K Bulley to A W Hill, 31 May 1914, *China−Plant Collns−cultural prods.* 1853−1914 (Kew).

20. A K Bulley to I B Balfour, 29 March 1914 (Edin.).

21. A K Bulley to I B Balfour, 1 March 1915 (Edin.).

22. Ibid. 14 June 1915.

23. R E Cooper Box Files (Edin.).
24. A K Bulley to I B Balfour, 11 September 1917 (Edin.).
25. R E Cooper Box Files (Edin.).
26. A K Bulley to I B Balfour, 20 June 1915 (Edin.).
27. Ibid. 9 January 1916.
28. Ibid. 6 February 1916.
29. Grierson, A J C, and Long, D G, *Flora of Bhutan* 1 RBGE 1983 pp.7–8; and with thanks to David Long for his help over Cooper. For seeds sent to Kew or Edinburgh, see Inwards Books (Kew) or Accessions Books (Edin.).
30. I B Balfour to A K Bulley, 13 June 1916 (Edin.).
31. I B Balfour to J C Williams, 8 September 1914, HERB/1/33/1D, 1914–15 (Edin.).

Chapter 7. Reginald Farrer in China and Burma

The author is grateful to Dr John and Mrs Joan Farrer for this exceptional opportunity to quote extensively from the letters of Reginald Farrer to his mother. They are kept in the private family archive and Mrs Joan Farrer has arranged the letters as far as possible in chronological order. All quotations in this chapter are from the Farrer family archive unless noted below. Any subsequent quotation from the Farrer archive must receive the consent of Dr and Mrs Farrer.

1. I B Balfour to D Prain, 25 April 1915, *Balfour, I Bayley corresp. Boxfile PRAIN, Sir David* (Edin.).
2. A K Bulley to I B Balfour, 30 December 1912 (Edin.).
3. G.C. 47, 1910, p.124.
4. G.C. 47, 1910, p.157.
5. *Bees' Cat.* No 41, Bees Ltd. Liverpool, 1913, p.5 (Edin.).
6. R Farrer to I B Balfour, 14 October 1914, HERB/9/4/1 (Edin.).
7. G.C. 55, 1914, p.360.
8. G.C. 56, 1914, p.28.
9. G.C. 56, 1914, p.116.
10. A K Bulley to I B Balfour, 1 March 1915 (Edin.).
11. I B Balfour to A K Bulley, 3 March 1915 (Edin.).
12. A K Bulley to I B Balfour, 8 April 1917 (Edin.).
13. I B Balfour to R Farrer, 28 September 1916, HERB/9/4/1 (Edin.).
14. Martineau, A, *The Herbaceous Garden* (4th edn), Williams & Norgate, 1934, p.72.
15. R Farrer to I B Balfour, 6 October 1916, HERB/9/4/1 (Edin.).
16. A K Bulley to E A Bowles, 28 October 1916, *Bowles corr.* (RHS).
17. R Farrer to I B Balfour, 13 May 1917, HERB/9/4/1 (Edin.).
18. I B Balfour to R Farrer, 8 August 1917, HERB/9/4/1 (Edin.).
19. Sassoon, S, 'Everyone Sang' in *The Oxford Book of War Poetry* (Stallworthy, J, ed.), Oxford University Press, 1987, p.178.
20. Graves, R, *Goodbye to All That*, Penguin Books, 1960, p.236.

21. R Farrer to E H M Cox, 25 June 1920, *Farrer corresp.* (Edin.).
22. Stearn, W T, ' Plant names commemorating Reginald Farrer' in *Reginald Farrer, Dalesman, Plant Hunter, Gardener* (Illingworth, J, and Routh, J, eds) Occ. Paper No.19, University of Lancaster, 1991, pp.43–54.
23. A K Bulley to E A Bowles, 18 May 1920 *Bowles Corr.* (RHS).

Chapter 8. Everest and After

1. A K Bulley to A R Hinks, 3 February 1992, *EE9/3/22* (RGS).
2. A K Bulley to F Younghusband, 25 February 1921, *EE9/2/1* (RGS).
3. A K Bulley to A R Hinks, 12 March 1921, *EE9/2/5* (RGS).
4. F K Ward to A R Hinks, 1 December 1921, *RGS Corr.* (Ward) 1921–30 (RGS).
5. Howard-Bury, C K, *Mount Everest: The Reconnaissance 1921*, Edward Arnold, 1922, p.291.
6. A R Hinks to F J Hanbury, 6 December 1921, *EE9/2/23* (RGS).
7. A K Bulley to A R Hinks, 27 November 1921 *EE9/2/16* (RGS).
8. 'An excursion from Mount Everest' by A F R Wollaston 1921 *EE3/1/60* (RGS).
9. A F R Wollaston to A W Hill, 7 March 1922, *Boxfile Balfour, I.Bayley Corr.* 1912–22 (Edin.).
10. A K Bulley to A R Hinks, 3 February 1922, *EE9/3/22* (RGS).
11. A K Bulley to A R Hinks, 20 February 1922, *EE9/3/42* (RGS).
12. Ibid.
13. Bruce, C G, *The Assault on Everest*, 1992, Edward Arnold, 1923, p.285.
14. A K Bulley to F C Stern, 4 May 1924, *F C Stern, F K Ward Misc. Letters* 13–21, (Kew).
15. Ibid. 8 May 1924.
16. *Annals of Botany XL*, 1926, p.541.
17. *Curtis's Botanical Magazine*, 1926, t9196.
18. Lyte, C, *Frank Kingdon-Ward*, John Murray, 1989, p.95.
19. A K Bulley to Kew, 17 August 1931, *F C Stern, F K Ward Misc. Letters* 19 (Kew).
20. A K Bulley to A Henry, 19 February 1926, *Henry mss* (Dub.).

Chapter 9. Snowdon: Conflict with Conservationists

1. Correvon, H, 'Natural Alpine Gardens' *Flora & Sylva* 3, 1905, p.53.
    2. A K Bulley to I B Balfour, 17 October 1915 (Edin.).
3. I B Balfour to A K Bulley, 17 November 1915 (Edin.).
4. A K Bulley to I B Balfour, 21 January 1916 (Edin.).
5. A K Bulley to D Prain, 22 February 1920, *Dir. Corr. (Eng. Letters)* 1911–20, 119, (Kew).
6. Ibid. 4 November 1920.
7. A K Bulley to D Prain, 23 July 1921, *Dir. Corr. (Eng. Letters)* 1921–28, (Kew).
8. A K Bulley to D Prain, 4 November 1920, *Dir. Corr. (Eng. Letters)* 1911–20, 119 (Kew).

9. A K Bulley to D Prain, 1 September 1921, Dir. Corr. (Eng. Letters) 1921–28 (Kew).

10. List of plants planted on Snowdon, 24 September 1921, Dir. Corr. (Eng. Letters) 1921–28 (Kew).

11. A K Bulley to D Prain, 17 October 1921, Dir. Corr. (Eng. Letters) 1921–28 (Kew).

12. Kew Bulletin No.8 1921 p.319.

13. A K Bulley to D Prain, 11 November 1921, Dir. Corr. (Eng. Letters) 1921–28 (Kew).

14. Ibid. 27 November 1921.

15. A K Bulley to I B Balfour, 16 December 1921 (Edin.).

16. 'Naturalising Alpine Plants on Snowdon' Editorial, Bull. AGS, 1933, pp.22–3.

17. Council Minutes of the Linnean Society, 27 October 1932, Item 13.

18. Kleiner, P, 'The alpine gardens of the Swiss Alps' Bull. AGS, 14, 1946, p.15.

19. I B Balfour to A K Bulley, 2 January 1922 (Edin.).

20. Condry, W M, The Snowdonia National Park, Collins, 1966, p.145.

21. Woodhead, N, 'Alpine Plants of the Snowdon Range' Bull. AGS, 2, 1933, p.12.

Chapter 10. The Persevering Plantsman

1. Advert. of Bees Ltd in Rock Gardens and Alpine Plants, T W Sanders (3rd edn), Collingridge.

2. Dunn Ewan J and N, Biographical Dictionary of Rocky Mountain Naturalists 1682–1932, 1981, Dr W Junk, pp.5, 160.

3. A K Bulley to I B Balfour, 1 March 1915 (Edin.).

4. Ibid. 28 January 1912.

5. Accessions, April 1913 and 27 November 1913 (Edin.).

6. A K Bulley to I B Balfour, 16 May 1915 (Edin.).

7. Ibid. 6 August 1916 (Edin.).

8. A K Bulley to D Prain, 1 July 1917, Dir. Corr. (Eng. Letters), 107, 1911–20 (Kew).

9. A K Bulley to I B Balfour, 11 September 1917 (Edin.).

10. Postcard from Dr Purpus to A K Bulley 23 December 1919, personal papers, Miss A L Bulley.

11. A K Bulley to I B Balfour, 18 January 1921 (Edin.).

12. A K Bulley to Mr Hill, 4 June 1924, Dir. Corr. (Eng. Letters) 125, 1921–28 (Kew).

13. Guiseppi, P L, 'Mr A K Bulley' obituary in Bull. AGS, 10 1942, p.248.

14. A L Bulley to K Hulme, 18 November 1985.

15. Guiseppi, P L, 'Mr A K Bulley', obituary in Bull. AGS, 10 1942, p.249.

16. I B Balfour to A K Bulley, 6 May 1912 (Edin.).

17. A K Bulley to D Prain, 15 July 1912, Dir. Corr. (Eng. Letters) 119, 1911–20 (Kew).

18. List of subscribers, in Comber, H F, Expdn to the Andes 1926, HERB/41/4/1 (Edin.).

19. H F Comber to H D McLaren, 12 October 1925, *Comber H F, Expdn to the Andes 1926, HERB/41/4/1* (Edin.).

20. C Elliott to W W Smith, in *Elliott, C, Expdn. to the Andes 1929–30. HERB/41/3/2* (Edin.).

21. Obituary of E K Balls, *The Times*, 9 November 1984 (Edin.).

22. E K Balls to J M Cowan, 27 September 1932, *E K Balls, Expdn. to Persia 1932 HERB/38/1/1* (Edin.).

23. Copies in the Library at Ness Botanic Gardens.

24. A K Bulley to F C Stern, 10 July 1931, *F C Stern – Paeonia mss.* 42 (Kew).

25. A K Bulley to F C Stern, 15 March 1932, *F C Stern – Purchase and Exchange of Plants* 1, 190 (Kew).

26. Letter from A K Bulley to F C Stern, 6 December 1933, *F C Stern – Purchase and Exchange of Plants* 1, 195 (Kew).

27. *Conference on Rock Gardens and Rock Plants*, RHS, 1936, p.93.

28. Gray, T, 'Elegy written in a Country Churchyard', in *The Centuries' Poetry*, vol.3, Penguin Books, 1942, p.64.

Chapter 11. Overview: Bulley's Contribution

1. McLean, B J, 'Plant Collecting and Patronage' in *Reginald Farrer, Dalesman, Plant Hunter, Gardener* (Illingworth, J, and Routh, J, eds) Occ. Paper No. 19, University of Lancaster, 1991, pp.15–19.

2. I B Balfour to J C Williams, 28 June 1919, HERB/1/33/1F (Edin.).

3. I B Balfour to A K Bulley, January 1922 (Edin.).

4. Briggs, R W, *'Chinese' Wilson*, HMSO, 1993, p.46.

5. Richards, J, *Primula*, Batsford, 1993, p.32.

6. Stern, F C, *A Study of the Genus Paeonia*, RHS, 1946, p.18.

7. Wright, W P, *An Illustrated Encyclopaedia of Gardening*, J M Dent & Sons, 1911, p.266.

8. Taylor, G C, 'The Asiatic Primulas' in Jekyll, G, *Wall, Water and Woodland Gardens* (8th edn), 1933, p.224.

Epilogue

1. A K Bulley to Mrs Mildred McLaren, 2 December 1901, personal papers of Miss A L Bulley, now in the University of Liverpool archives.

2. Leigh, M S, *A History of the Whishaw Family*, Methuen, 1935.

3. BBC North Regional Broadcast, 7.00 p.m., 13 February 1934.

Arthur Kilpin Bulley
1861–1942
A Chronicle

1861	Born in New Brighton, Cheshire.
1868	Goes to Mostyn House School, Parkgate, Cheshire.
1874	On to Marlborough College.
1879	Enters his father's firm, S M Bulley & Son, cotton brokers.
1886	Becomes partner of S M Bulley & Son and member of The Liverpool Cotton Association Ltd.
1890	Marries Harriet Agnes Whishaw. They live at Riversdale House, Riversdale Road, West Kirby.
1895	Move to 28 Darmonds Green, West Kirby.
1897–8	Buys land at Ness. House built.
1898	Move to Mickwell Brow, Ness, Neston, Cheshire.
1898–1904	Builds stables, sheds, glass houses. Begins to create shelter belts, woodland, rock garden, herbaceous borders. 'Bulley's Gardens' open to the public.
1904	Asks Professor Balfour for a plant collector. George Forrest is suggested. Bulley funds him and launches his career. 'Ness Nurseries' of A Bee & Co starts in garden.
1905	Nursery named Co-operative Bees Ltd.
1906	Nursery becomes Bees Ltd.
1910	Funds Forrest's second expedition to Yunnan, China.
1910	Stands as a Women's Suffrage candidate, Rossendale.
1910–12	Stands for Labour in three municipal elections, Liverpool.
1911	Bees Ltd expands to Sealand. Bulley launches Frank Kingdon Ward's plant collecting in China and Tibet.
1913	Josiah Hope, head gardener, converts nursery to amenity gardens and modifies the rock garden. Bulley funds Roland Cooper to collect in Sikkim and then Bhutan.
1914	First offer to fund Reginald Farrer in Kansu, China.
1916	Funds six-week collector in California.
1919	Funds Forrest, Ward and Farrer.

1920	Provides bowling greens, tennis courts, playing fields.
1921	Experiments with foreign arctic and alpine species on Snowdonia and causes controversy.
1921–2	Invests in two Everest expeditions for seeds.
1922	Elected to Victoria Medal of Honour (VMH) by RHS but declines it. Retires from S M Bulley & Son.
1923	Winters in South Africa.
1924	World Tour, including New Zealand and Australia.
1925–6	Joins syndicate for H F Comber in Argentina.
1925–7	W Siehe collects for him in Asia Minor.
1929–30	Subscribes to syndicate for Clarence Elliott to Chile.
1932/3/5	Shares in syndicates for E K Balls in Persia and Turkey.
1934	North Regional broadcast 'The Fascination of Alpines'.
1937	Share in syndicate for E K Balls in Greece.
1942	Dies at Mickwell Brow.

Chinese Place Names

The spelling of Chinese place names has often varied, but since the time of Bulley and his plant hunters the official system for transcription has completely changed. In the text of this book the names are those used at the time. The following lists show the names currently accepted.

Names used at the time of Bulley	Names used today
PROVINCES AND AUTONOMOUS REGIONS	
Kansu	Gansu
Shansi	Shanxi
Szechuan	Sichuan
Tibet	Xizang
Yunnan	Yunnan
CITIES AND TOWNS	
Atuntze, Atuntse, Atuntsi	Dechen, Deqen, Deqin, Dequn
Chengtu	Chengdu
Tali, Talifu	Dali
Tachien-lu, Tatsien-lu	Kangding
Yunnan-fu	Kunming
Lanchow	Lanzhou
Lhasa	Lhasa
Lichiang, Likiang	Lijiang
Mengtze, Mengsi	Mengzi
Ningpo	Ningbo
Szemao	Simao
Tengyueh	Tengchong
RIVERS AND LAKES	
Koko Nor	Qinghai Hu
Lake Tali-fu	Erhai
Mekong	Lancang Jiang
Salween, Salwin	Nu Jiang
Yangtze (upper)	Jinsha Jiang
Yangtze (lower)	Chang Jiang
Yellow	Huang He

MOUNTAINS

Chungtien plateau	Zhongdian
Lichiang mountains	Yulong Shan
Mount Omei	Emei Shan
Tali mountains	Cang Shan

Chinese Plants Named After A K Bulley and Bees Ltd

A K BULLEY

Genus
Bulleyia yunnanensis Schltr

Species (some names are synonyms)
Aconitum bulleyanum Diels
*Adenophora bulleyana Diels
Agapetes bulleyana Diels
Allium bulleyanum Diels
Aleuritia bulleyana (Forrest) J. Sojak
Anaphalis bulleyana (Jeffrey) Hand.-Mazz
Androsace bulleyana Forrest
Aster bulleyanus Jeffrey
*Codonopsis bulleyana Forrest ex Diels
Corydalis bulleyana Diels
Crawfurdia bulleyana Forrest
*Delphinium bulleyanum Forrest ex Diels
Dendrobium bulleyi Rolfe
*Diapensia bulleyana Forrest ex Diels
*Gentiana bulleyana (Forrest) Marquand
Euphorbia bulleyana Diels
Habenaria bulleyi Rolfe
Hemipilia bulleyi Rolfe
Herminium bulleyi (Rolfe) Tang & Wang
*Iris bulleyana Dykes
Isodon bulleyanus Kudo
Morina bulleyana Forrest ex Diels
Peristylus bulleyi (Rolfe) K. Y. Lang
Plectranthus bulleyanus Diels
Pluchea bulleyana Jeffrey
*Primula bulleyana Forrest
Rabdosia bulleyana (Diels) Hara

BEES LTD

Genus
Beesia calthaefolia (Maxim) Balf. et
    W. W. Sm. (syn. B. cordata)
Beesia deltophylla C. Y. Wu

Species (some names are synonyms)
Aleuritia beesiana (Forrest) J. Sojak
*Allium beesianum W. W. Smith
Amitostigma beesianum (W. W. Smith)
    T. Tang & F. T. Wang
Berberis beesiana Ahrendt
Bergenia beesiana Hort. ex C. Schneider
Chaetoseris beesiana (Diels) C. Shih
Comastoma beesianum (W. W. Smith)
    Holub
Delphinium beesianum W. W. Smith
Gentiana beesiana W. W. Smith
Gentianella beesiana (W. W. Smith)
    Holub
Habenaria beesiana W. W. Smith
*Jasminum beesianum Forrest ex Diels
Lactuca beesiana Diels
Orchis beesiana W. W. Smith
Ponerorchis beesiana (W. W. Smith) Soo
*Primula beesiana Forrest
Rhinacanthus beesianus Diels
*Rhododendron beesianum Diels
Rhyncanthus beesianus W. W. Smith

Hybrids and cultivars
*Armeria 'Bees' Ruby'
*Clematis 'Bees' Jubilee'

A K BULLEY (continued)

Species (some names are synonyms)
*Salvia bulleyana Diels
Saxifraga bulleyana Engl. & Irmscher
*Senecio bulleyanus Diels
Tripterospermum bulleyanum (Forrest)
     Raiz
Vaccinium bulleyanum (Diels) Sleum

Variety
*Polygala calcarea var. bulleyana (Bulley's
     form)

*Recently grown in Britain
The author is grateful to the Trustees of the RBG Kew for use of the Index Kewensis on CD-ROM.

BEES LTD (continued)

Hybrids and cultivars
*Incarvillea mairei 'Bees' Pink'
*Lobelia 'Bees' Flame'
*Potentilla fruticosa 'Beesii'
  Roscoea 'Beesiana'

Index

Page references in *italics* indicate illustrations, in **bold** preceded by **Pl.** indicate plates.

Printed in the United Kingdom for The Stationery Office
N14290 C20 5/97 (2844)